Exploring Yoga
and Cancer

With kind regards, ॐ and prem

Exploring Yoga and Cancer

Dr Swami Yogapratap

Yoga Publications Trust, Munger, Bihar, India

Published by Yoga Publications Trust
    First edition 2009

ISBN: 978-81-86336-83-0

Publisher and distributor: Yoga Publications Trust, Ganga Darshan, Munger, Bihar, India.

Website: www.biharyoga.net
          www.rikhiapeeth.net

Printed at Thomson Press (India) Limited, New Delhi, 110001

Dedication

*In humility we offer this dedication to
Swami Sivananda Saraswati, who initiated
Swami Satyananda Saraswati into the secrets of yoga.*

Contents

Preface

Surprising as it may seem, today both yoga and cancer share one common attribute – both are common household names and familiar to one and all. The difference, of course, is that people want more and more of the former and less and less of the latter! Be that as it may, there is no denying the fact that cancer is on the rampage and if the latest statistics are to be believed, one in three to five people stand the risk of contracting cancer during their lifetime. With figures as scary as those, one is tempted to say that we are in the grip of an epidemic, nay, verily a pandemic of cancer. It has become a topic of concern for all healthcare providers the world over. The incidence of cancer has grown exponentially over the decades and has reached alarming proportions, causing enormous and widespread suffering.

Tons of research has gone into unravelling the mystery of cancer. Yet, the solution seems as elusive as trying to locate the rat amongst its underground maze of rat burrows in a field. As we manage to locate one and seal it off, we come across still another offshoot leading yet elsewhere, and of course the rat is nowhere to be seen. A herculean task with no end in sight! Almost every tissue in the entire body is susceptible to contracting cancer, and once cancer takes root, it can spread almost everywhere. And when we manage to come up with some treatment module, the disease ups the ante by releasing newer tricks and subverting the efficacy of the treatment. Clearly, it is an uphill task even if we do not take into consideration the pain, agony and trauma inflicted on patients and the lifelong gut wrenching and helpless situation of the relatives who have no option but to see their beloved ones fall prey to the ravages of cancer.

Perhaps that is why Swami Satyananda felt it necessary to elucidate the role of yoga in the management of this vast pandemic. When I was entrusted with the task of writing a book on yoga and cancer, my main problem was not what to include, but quite the opposite. I needed to decide what not to include! I realized that we are so over-bombarded with facts, articles and information about cancer that we are literally suffering from information overload. It becomes very hard to sift through and to pick and choose the right facts and to make the correct decisions. Here again, the advice of Swami Satyasangananda came to my rescue. She advised me not to get caught up in the maze of information, but to think as a doctor and approach yoga as a doctor (not as a medical professional), analyze it and present cancer in a yogic perspective. And that is precisely what I found to be most useful. I used the minimalistic approach and have concentrated on the concepts and principles rather than worrying about research quotations. Thanks to the widespread use of the internet, which is now available to one and all, information about research quotations can easily be had by those interested, at the click of the mouse.

My earlier medical and surgical experience in dealing with cancer patients, especially those undergoing cancer surgeries, also stood me in good stead here. Patients, after their initial shock, trauma, denial and guilt at having cancer, I recalled, always wanted to know what cancer exactly is and why it is caused, so that they can also be in a better position to understand the magnitude of the problem and devise means to ease the situation. They were not interested in grand theories and postulates. Their objective was simple. They wanted something practical and real to manage the situation and help tide them over the crisis and get them back into the mainstream of the society. Getting cancer meant that they were racing against time. Their questions were no-nonsense, direct and to the point. For them, the countdown had not only begun, but was nearing completion. Time suddenly was at a high premium. Their priorities were reversed almost overnight: they had their lives at stake after all.

Many of the patients did not know exactly what cancer was and were very inquisitive about its details. "Doctor, but *why* did I get cancer when I never did anything wrong?" and "*What* is it that actually happens to me in cancer and *how* does it happen?" That, I reasoned, would be the logical starting point. Keeping these requirements in mind, I went to task, started with the bare facts and built up the castle piece by piece, trying to logically derive the next step from the first. This comprises Part 1 of the book wherein we explore the concept of disease in general and cancer specifically, and get into the nitty-gritties of the disease, which remain the same, no matter where it is located in the patient. The objective here is to familiarize the reader with the various aspects of the body, disease and cancer formation with the basic assumption that the reader is generally unfamiliar with these concepts. For those who are already conversant with these topics could find it worthwhile to take a second look at the facts. For these nuggets of information are like the pieces of a jigsaw puzzle; each separate unit makes perfect sense yet refuses to fit into a smooth complete picture. Often we need to develop a new perspective towards the same old facts, so that they can make sense when seen as a whole.

Expounding on yoga in a non-classical style, yet retaining its essence, became the next requirement; how can one use yoga without understanding the ABC of yoga? Although yoga is widely practised today, the information available is more about the simpler avenues of yoga and the practices contained therein. To be able to use the entire repertoire of yoga, it becomes imperative to understand yoga, its roots and the basic concepts which form the building blocks of this vast system.

Part 2 focuses on this aspect. In medicine, we understand a specific disease by studying the anatomy, physiology and pathology of the related organs. Anatomy has to do with the structural details of the body, physiology with the functions, and pathology with the abnormal anatomy during disease. The doctor in me came to the fore and tried to dissect yoga layer by layer in a similar manner, break it down into basic units and present it accordingly. Only after having analyzed the disease from all possible angles, do we go in to speak about the solution. This forms the core of Part 2.

After having understood both yoga and cancer separately with reasonable details, the time was ripe to mix them together and come up with some exotic recipes for cancer management and prevention! Part 3 speaks of yogic management of cancer and some possible methods by which one can manage cancer if one has already contracted it and prevent it if one is fortunate enough to not to have had a brush with cancer.

Part 4 gives a bird's eye view on the various related research being done in relation to yoga and cancer. The aim is to arm the reader with the related information so that he or she can take the initiative and participate in the process. Research is basically a refined search and analysis of any phenomenon. The reader should perform his or her own analysis and use his or her own grey cells to make observations, draw inferences from them and re-evaluate the phenomenon in this new light. This is how research was performed in the olden days by the rishis of ancient India, and it is most liberating and satisfying to be able to walk in their footsteps, a step at a time.

The final proof of the pudding lies in its eating. No amount of discussions, debates and reams of paper can replace the bliss of enjoying the experience of eating a well cooked delicious pudding. Similarly, the efficacy of a treatment, no matter how sound logically and in theory, lies in its practical application and success in reality. In fact, many such natural means of treatment have been used in part for decades by many individuals and even many health care providers, but it is yoga that provides a systematic, integrated, rational and multidimensional approach, having a scientific, logical and theoretically sound base. As early as the 1950s, Marguerite Bugler from France discovered the self-healing power of the body, using yoga, dietetics and natural means to overcome cancer and live a normal productive life. Her personal experience and account is included in Appendix 3 and serves to remind us of others who have already performed this experiment and reached the same conclusions. It is a tale of courage and resolve and inspires us to emulate the same in our lives. Such miraculous and courageous tales abound in the annals of cancer. If someone has been able to reach the destination while groping in darkness, we can surely do the same when guided properly, can't we? And that is also one of the aims of yoga . . . to help us explore our own potentials and live them fully.

1: The Nature and Causes of Cancer

1

Yoga, Disease and Cancer: An Introduction

We live in remarkable times. Advances in information technology and telecommunications have ushered in the era of the global village. Tremendous developments in medical science, including the discovery of antibiotics in the early twentieth century, have brought age-old scourges such as malaria, typhoid, plague and pneumonia under control. Diseases which previously devastated entire generations need no longer be regarded with dread. Through coordinated vaccination programs, smallpox has been eliminated from the world's population. No wonder it seemed that man had finally won the age-old battle with nature to conquer the ravages of disease. Things which were possible only in the dreams and fiction of our parents and grandparents are routine events today.

The story, however, does not end there. Difficult to treat diseases such as cancer and auto-immune syndromes, some previously unknown, have come to the fore. Overcoming them, and improving the quality of life for those suffering their effects, has become a very real and increasingly difficult challenge in today's times.

In spite of all the research that has gone into understanding the disease process that is cancer, our understanding of the disease remains far from complete. Without doubt the rapid advances in treatment options have dramatically improved the five-year survival rate in some types of cancer, but even these regimens are unfortunately not able to provide a cure. In the desperate search for a cancer cure, multiple modalities have sprung up.

On closer analysis, it becomes apparent that the multitude of modalities emerging for the treatment of cancer are actually a reflection of a deeper reality. They point to the fact that in spite of all the research and astounding advances in the field of oncology (the study of cancer), our knowledge of cancer, its origins, causes, triggers and mechanisms, is far from complete and coherent. The shortcoming is not in the depth of knowledge, but in an inability to widen our horizons when considering the disease. The following analogy illustrates this.

The panorama seen from the first storey of a high rise building is vastly different to that seen from the top storey. Our understanding of the situation and consequently our responses to it are dramatically affected by that difference. Decisions based on the information gathered from the first storey view will be incomplete and hence insufficient to bring the desired results. Suppose a person on the street is waiting for you to provide instructions about the exact road to take. From the first storey you may not see that there is a car coming along the road as it is beyond your horizon. From the seventh storey, however, you can not only see the car coming, but also the snarling dog on the left corner! This information will certainly alter the instructions you give about which path to take. In the same way, we need to widen our horizons to be able to gain a better understanding of cancer and consequently the most appropriate method to deal with it successfully.

Today, cancer remains amongst the top killers in the developed world. Unlike many diseases, cancer is not a single disease entity with a single cure. It is, in fact, a disease process which can affect almost any part of the body with disastrous and unpredictable consequences. This book will help you to understand cancer, and explore some of the options available for managing and curing cancer while leading a successful, well-integrated and fulfilling life. Yoga provides powerful tools which help to achieve these objectives

4

either in conjunction with conventional therapies or on its own. Yoga acts as a tool, not only for the management of cancer, but may also help to prevent the onset of cancer.

What is yoga?

Yoga needs no introduction today. It has permeated the very fabric of society spanning all races, creeds and countries. It is being practised all over the world for good health, for excellence in performance, as a therapy and for a wide range of other purposes. This is a far cry from a mere five decades ago when misconceptions about yoga were common. Yoga has now rightly found its place as a respected science with wide applications for the benefit of humanity. It is inadequate, however, to limit the concept of yoga to physical exercises or breathing practices, or even to a few practices for calming the never-ending cacophony of the mind. Yoga is much more than just that – it is a way of life. The modern way of life includes wonders, comforts and unprecedented conveniences at the physical level, yet it has also wrought a deep disharmony in our bodies, mind, emotions and in our subtler selves.

There is a great deal of incongruence between the demands the modern lifestyle makes on our body relative to its capabilities and rhythms which developed through evolution over many millennia. Yoga has the potential to bridge this gap and optimize the body-mind unit to give its best performance.

The cacophony of diseases which afflict the body-mind can, and need to be, converted into a soul-stirring and satisfying piece of music. Only then can we enjoy a positive, constructive and contributing life. This book endeavours to understand yoga in all its various forms and discuss the use of certain practices for the management of the different stages and types of cancer.

What exactly is a disease?

Cancer is one of many diseases affecting human beings today. The simplest definition of disease is contained in the word itself: it is derived from the Old French *desaise*, meaning 'lack of ease'. 'Dys' implies an inability, inappropriateness or a non-functional state of the organism to varying degrees. 'Ease' implies a condition of perfect harmony and coordination in the body-mind, so that there is minimal tension while carrying out the various functions and activities required of it. Any state in which this is not possible, and from which the body-mind is apparently unable to revert to its earlier state, indicates disease.

The ancient seers of India realized that human existence is far more complex than that which is visible to our eyes. They likened the human system to a chariot with five horses. The chariot is a finely tuned and efficient mechanical structure enabling us to cover long distances over extended periods of time without undue difficulties. Five excellent, expert, strong and skilled horses, the senses, pull this chariot. This forms the first dimension of the body-mind complex. The next dimension consists of the charioteer or driver, who directs the entire chariot, expertly taking it to its destination as desired by the next and third dimension of the structure – the passenger. These three main components are very closely correlated and any loss of communication or miscommunication between them will result in disharmony and consequently an accident.

The passenger may want to go to the west, the charioteer might be goading the horses on towards the east and the horses, on seeing lush green grass in the south and north, try to rush in those directions! Where such confusion leads is anybody's guess. Only a fine line divides the soul-stirring music of an orchestra from a harsh cacophony. It takes only a small error in timing to turn the former into the latter, as many who learn music can readily testify. Similarly, even a small error at any one of the three tiers can wreak havoc in this human system and result in permanent damage. This damage or loss of efficiency manifests as an illness or disease.

Yoga takes the body-mind paradigm one step further and speaks of the body-mind-spirit triad. The body is the vehicle or interface between the spirit-mind and the external

6

environment. It receives sensory impulses and conveys them to the brain where they are registered and processed. The mind then interprets these signals and indicates the course of action to be taken. Accordingly, the brain relays messages to the relevant cells or organs and implements the suggested course of action. The mind thus acts as the driver of the vehicle. The spirit is the passenger, who decides on the destination.

Cross-communication and poor coordination amongst these three is at the root of many, if not all, the problems that arise in our lives. Whether on the socio-political, economic, personal, emotional, mental or physical level, all the difficulties we face ultimately boil down to this simple cause – disharmony within this triad. Prolonged and repeated disturbances cause dysfunction in the human system, resulting in malfunction. As Swami Sivananda puts it, there is disharmony between the head, heart and hands, causing illnesses to manifest.

The causes of disease in the system (spanning the body-mind-spirit triad) vary, depending on which part of the system is unbalanced. Diseases can, therefore, be classified along these lines as somatic, psycho-somatic and psychic. Further classifications can take place depending on the nature of the disease, the causative agent, the part affected and the outcome expected or the prognosis. However, from the yogic point of view, all diseases originate from an imbalance in the body-mind-spirit triad, leading to reduced efficiency and output.

What is cancer?

The word cancer strikes terror in one and all. Mention of this dreaded C-word at a doctor's consultation brings out one's deepest fears and wreaks havoc in one's entire life. What exactly is cancer? And why does it inspire such dread?

Cancer is a disease which can manifest in virtually any part of the body. It is basically caused by the malfunctioning of the most basic unit of the body – the cell. There is a serious and apparently irreparable loss of the normal cycle of cell formation, maturation, growth and functioning, which results in the uncontrolled growth of one or more abnormal cell types. The cells grow and divide at abnormal rates and may then spread beyond the original site. This continues unabated while the rest of the body suffers and starts wasting away.

According to yoga, certain strong, unbalancing forces can cause cancer. These forces, which can also be considered to be the causative factors of cancer, are seen to have a similar pattern of action. They affect us on all dimensions: physical, mental, emotional, intellectual and psychic. Some originate on the physical level, such as tobacco chewing, infections by certain viruses, exposure to radiation, etc., while others originate from the deeper layers of ourselves: for example, emotional factors, stress factors, lifestyle factors and so on. All these factors have their own mechanism of action by which they cause cancer, be it from the physical plane, mental, emotional or psychic plane.

According to yoga, ultimately all these factors exert strong unbalancing pressures and cause some fundamental and similar changes, which if left uncorrected can lead to the formation of cancer. These forces are usually recurring in nature, cause repeated injury and exert a powerful influence on the body-mind. This ultimately leads to genetic changes in the body which lead to cancer. These factors cause irreparable damage to the system and manifest as a dysfunction in the fundamental aspect of the body – the cell. The core within the cell, the DNA, becomes modified, causing the cell to malfunction and to multiply at a much higher and uncontrolled rate, without regard for the needs and requirements of the body. Such malfunctioning cells are the manifestation of these disruptive forces and the end result is the disease called 'cancer'.

Yoga and disease management
In order to restore the balance of the body-mind-spirit triad, we need to find the link or connection between the three pillars of this triad. Disease manifests in the system when

there is disharmony between the body, the mind and the spirit. If we follow this chain of thought further, then we come to the conclusion that the only true and lasting solution is the removal of the imbalance caused in this triad and a re-establishment of harmony amongst these three components.

This is the crux of the problem, and once you strike at the root of the problem and remove it, the entire tree, no matter how massive it may appear to be, withers away. Yoga, through the action of its diverse practices, can deal with the basis, or source, of these imbalances. It provides the possibility of changing the patterns in the body-mind. The changes yoga can bring about are able to correct the imbalances and return the system to normal. This is the role of yoga in disease and the reason why it has worked magic in the lives of millions of people around the globe.

Summarizing, cancer has many causes, including ones related to environment and lifestyle which lead to various genetic changes in a person. Over a period of time, these changes reach a critical level and can then manifest in the body as a cancerous growth. In the following chapters we will explore the complexities of cancer in detail, and try to gain a better understanding of its causes and the rationale behind the management of cancer.

2

Cancer: An Overview

Cancer is a multifactorial, degenerative, debilitating disorder affecting millions across the globe. It spans all segments of society, regardless of wealth, race or continent. For this reason there is a need to delve deeper into cancer and the mechanism of its causation. In so doing we can gain a deeper understanding of both life and the root cause of cancer. Only with the benefit of this new knowledge can we have the clarity to act effectively in relation to the threat of cancer and for a better future. From the yogic point of view, while nutritional and environmental factors do play a role, physiological, social, emotional, psychological, and spiritual factors are also important. Bearing this in mind, let us meet our enemy up front and at close quarters.

What really causes cancer? Is it caused by a virus or a genetic code, is it hereditary, is it due to the effect of carcinogens on the cells, or by a weakened immune system? Does a 'cancer-promoting' diet cause cancer? Or does it have to do with the psychological factors influenced by stress, poor attitude, or low self-esteem? While it is impossible to be sure at this stage, it does seem that cancer may be linked to all of these.

A discussion of cancer risk factors could easily fill a book, so bear in mind that the information presented here is an overview only. First we need to understand exactly what happens in our bodies when cancer develops. Let us begin by understanding the structure of the cell, the fundamental unit of our bodies, which is also the place where the pro-cancerous forces finally act to cause cancer.

The normal cell

The cell is the structural and functional unit of living organisms. Cells of similar type are organized into aggregations called tissue (e.g. muscle and bone) or into organs, semi-independent units performing a special function. Organs such as the lungs, colon, heart, liver, breast and brain consist of specialized cells that carry out the organ's functions. While every cell of the body shares common basic functions, cells of the various organs differentiate so as to be able to perform the necessary specific role. Thus a liver cell is markedly different from a heart cell, for example.

Fig. 2.1: The Cell

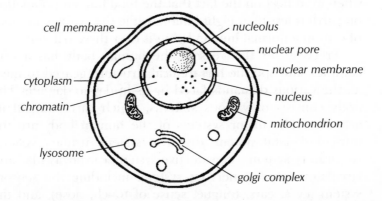

To ensure the proper performance of each organ, worn out or injured cells need to be replaced by new cells performing exactly the same function as the earlier ones. Repair and regeneration need to occur according to the needs of the body and this is ensured by a variety of mechanisms, including chemical messengers called 'growth factors' which trigger cell growth.

11

The human body is comprised of over three trillion cells. Each cell has a specific function to carry out and needs to work in precise and close coordination with the rest of the body. To understand the logistics better, the human body can be likened to a very complex and gigantic corporation with a workforce of over three trillion people. For a business of this magnitude to function efficiently and deliver successfully, it must have an incredibly fine-tuned and expert panel, including the CEO, administrators, managers, controllers, supervisors and innumerable workers to carry out the many activities. There need to be well-defined departments with clear and precise duties and work procedures. Proper communication channels, work protocols, disaster management principles and most importantly a clear, unambiguous blueprint of the motto of the company, which must be adhered to by everyone, no matter who they are. The complexity of the situation is further put into perspective when we reflect on the fact that the total human population on earth is less than eight billion, while the average number of cells in a normal human being is over three trillion!

Precisely for this reason, the human body has a very complex and specific hierarchical structure geared to meet all the various demands faced by us in day-to-day life. The body consists of various systems, which carry out all its activities. The major systems of the human body are the musculoskeletal system, digestive system, urinary system, respiratory system, reproductive system, cardiovascular and circulatory system, nervous system, including the sensory system (eyes, ears, tongue, sense of touch, nose), and the endocrine (hormonal) system.

Each system is assigned a specific task or set of tasks to be performed for the benefit of the entire organism. It is imperative that each system performs its assigned task to perfection for the proper functioning of the body. To do this, each system comprises many organs which have specific sub-tasks. Each organ has specialized tissues which are made up of innumerable cells. The cell is the last fundamental sub-unit of this hierarchy, and it can function independently in the same manner as the entire body itself, although it is normally controlled by the body's system of chemical messengers.

Let us now re-assemble the pack of cards, using a bottom-up approach this time. Life began on earth many millennia ago as a simple, single cellular organism. It managed to extract nutrition from the surrounding environment by means of simple modifications of the cell membrane (the outer envelope of the cell). When the organism was hungry, it moved itself to a location where nutrition was available and then used its cell membrane to gradually engulf the nutritive material. Various *organelles* (sub-units within the cell) responsible for breaking down this nutritive material into its basic components would then attach to this newly engulfed globule of food. They would release enzymes and chemicals for digesting the food. Once all the useful material had been digested, the waste would be thrown out of the cell simply by this globule being moved to the periphery of the cell, and being attached to the cell membrane from inside. Ejection or excretion, the reverse process of engulfment, would then take place, flushing the globule of waste into the outside environment.

As evolution progressed, it turned out that the efficiency of a two-celled organism was higher than that of a single-celled organism, as both the cells were able to carry out all the necessary functions more efficiently in coordination with each other. This cycle of multiplication continued and the single cell graduated into a multi-cellular organism with many cells just like itself, all conglomerated together as one whole unit. They continued to evolve, so that instead of each cell carrying out the same activity, specific duties were performed by each one, thereby reducing the time and energy consumed – a distinct advantage for survival.

Each cell was no longer required to go searching for food, ingesting and digesting it. Nor was it practical to do so. For example, ejecting the waste product out of the cell into the environment would, in this changed scenario, mean that one cell would throw its excreta into another cell, which would have the responsibility for excretion, for now each cell was no longer in direct contact with the outside environment. In this example, the original cell was *totipotent*, having the ability to develop into all cell types. Specialized cells had undergone a process of *differentiation*. It is important to understand that the original embryonic cells of a human being are totipotent, and then as the foetus grows in the womb, they gradually differentiate in order to perform various specific functions.

Differentiation necessarily means that the cells give up their totipotency or ability to perform all types of tasks and only then are able to concentrate on the task entrusted to them. In other words, a cell becomes known as a digestive or respiratory or immune or muscle cell not just because it is able to do that specific task, but because it is no longer able to do any other task. This process of specialization continues and specialized cells form specific tissues, which can form certain organs, which in turn constitute parts of various systems. All the systems together, under the control of a central regulating, controlling and cognizing principle, come to be known as the individual being.

DNA – the blueprint

Certain explicit governing rules and orders need to be laid down to ensure that each cell follows the master plan to the letter and does not deviate from it, for in such a highly complex organization, it is imperative that each cell carries out the tasks assigned to it. Failure to do so would have disastrous effects, not only for that particular cell, but for the whole organism. Hence, blueprints of the entire master plan are made and a copy of that is supplied to each cell to ensure that it has the necessary know-how to take up the responsibility assigned to it. This amazing component of biology is known as the organism's deoxyribonucleic acid (DNA) – the genetic material contained in each cell. All aspects of cell division,

14

multiplication and function are governed by the DNA, which allows for dynamic management, depending on the prevailing circumstances and needs. DNA is a highly complex molecule within the cell nucleus that serves as the cell's 'brain'. DNA is the blueprint for everything the cell does.

In a human cell, the DNA is arranged in 46 distinct sections called chromosomes. They are arranged in 23 pairs, and 23 chromosomes come from each biological parent. Together, the 46 chromosomes contain more than 100,000 genes. A gene is a segment of DNA that controls a specific cellular function. Each gene occupies a specific location in a chromosome. Through a number of biochemical steps, some genes instruct the cell to manufacture structural proteins which serve as building blocks. Other genes tell the cell to produce hormones or chemical growth factors which leave the cell and communicate with other cells. Still other genes tell the cell to produce regulatory proteins that tell other genes when to turn 'on' or 'off'. When a gene is turned on, it manufactures another complex molecule called ribonucleic acid (RNA), which is used to relay information between the DNA and the protein-producing apparatus of a cell.

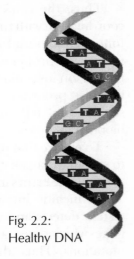

Fig. 2.2: Healthy DNA

Recent advances in genetics and cell behaviour have proved beyond doubt that the relationship between the nucleus or DNA matter and the cell is not just one-way traffic with the nucleus autocratically ordering the cell to follow its dictums according to the blueprint coded within it. The cell, which is in close contact with its surroundings, has a constant exchange of information with the nucleus about the status of the cell environment and hence the needs and expected future needs. The DNA accordingly produces proteins, for example, an enzyme or an antibody, capable of fulfilling that

15

need. This close two-way communication between the DNA and the rest of the cell is essential for the maintenance of proper cell health. If the cell starts sending erroneous messages to the DNA, this results in the production of erroneous proteins not appropriate to the current condition.

Thus, the cell's DNA controls all its activities in close coordination with the needs of the entire body and according to the signals sent by the body. Cells multiply only when they receive the proper signals from growth factors. For example, if a person loses blood, a growth factor called erythropoietin, which is produced in the kidneys, increases in the bloodstream, and tells the bone marrow to manufacture more blood cells.

To ensure that the cell complies with the overall plan and to safeguard against slip-ups, a number of mechanisms exist to minimize errors in the regulation of cellular multiplication. These include immune surveillance (in which the immune system detects and destroys abnormal cells) and specialized genes which detect and repair DNA damage and thus prevent mutations. Thus, the entire organism works with extreme efficiency under this system of mutual interdependence and checks and controls.

Cell energetics – normal cells

All cellular activities need energy without which none of the activity would be possible. The cell derives its energy from chemical reactions. Chemicals are made up of specific molecules, which in turn are made up of specific atoms. For example, one molecule of water is made up of two atoms of hydrogen and one atom of oxygen (H_2O). These atoms are held together by electro-chemical bonds. In general, the formation of chemical bonds requires energy which is released when these bonds are broken. In other words, some chemical bonds are high energy bonds while others are low energy bonds.

The cell uses a certain chemical known as adenosine triphosphate (ATP) as its standard currency of energy. A unit of ATP has three phosphate molecules attached by electro-chemical bonds to an adenosine component. When the cell needs energy, a phosphate molecule is cleaved from the ATP unit and the energy that was stored in the bond between the phosphate and the adenosine is made available for cellular activities. ATP can also release two phosphate molecules at a time, making energy available in the same way.

Conversely, in order to produce ATP, the cell acquires a suitable fuel (such as glucose) and breaks this fuel molecule down. In this breakdown, energy is released. In simple terms, this energy is used to produce a molecule of ATP by forming the bond that attaches a phosphate molecule to adenosine diphosphate (ADP). Thus ATP can be considered a way of storing energy within the cell, much as a battery stores energy.

The most commonly used fuel for energy production in the body is glucose. Fats and proteins are used less commonly. In general terms, there are two main mechanisms by which a molecule of glucose provides energy. In the presence of oxygen, glucose undergoes a series of chemical reactions that release energy. About 36 molecules of ATP are produced per molecule of glucose broken down. This process is known as aerobic respiration. It is a slower process than anaerobic respiration, which takes place in the absence of oxygen. In anaerobic respiration only two molecules of ATP are generated per glucose molecule. In this process, the glucose molecule creates lactic acid in addition to carbon dioxide and energy.

3

Understanding Cancer

Cancer can be understood as a cellular dysfunction in which a cell starts showing errant features, which cause it to divide and multiply at an abnormal rate. These cells are functionally and structurally immature to varying degrees, often being rudimentary and having failed to develop the differentiating characteristics of the original cell type. The cells tend to multiply at a much more rapid pace than is normal. They fail to respond to the normal mechanisms that control cell division and multiplication – this failure is known as the phenomenon of *autonomy*. They tend to show a marked propensity to invade surrounding normal tissues. They may also spread to distant sites, giving rise to multiple areas of abnormal cells (known as *metastasis*). A cancerous growth contains these abnormal cells, as well as a supporting structure of connective tissue and blood vessels. It is thought that the term *cancer* is derived from the Latin term for crab, because a cancer adheres to any part that it seizes upon in the obstinate manner of a crab.

Unlike normal cells, the mechanism of programmed cell death (*apoptosis*) can fail in cancer cells, making them almost literally immortal. In addition, these cells differ from normal cells in the manner of their metabolism. They tend to use metabolic processes which require an abnormal amount of glucose to provide their energy needs.

A cancer cell grows without any controls, checks or counterchecks. Unlike normal cells, cancer cells ignore signals

18

to stop dividing, to specialize, or to die and be shed. Growing in an uncontrolled manner and unable to recognize natural boundaries, the cancer cells may spread to areas of the body where they do not belong.

In a cancer cell, genetic mutations within the cell's DNA cause the cell to become defective. Cancer-causing genes are often called *oncogenes*. An example of an oncogene is a mutated gene that produces a defective protein which causes the growth-factor receptor on a cell's surface to act as if it is 'on' when in fact no growth factor is present. The result is that the cell receives a constant message to divide.

It is these attributes of a cancer cell that enable it to wreak so much havoc in the body. To help us comprehend the magnitude of the changes brought about by these attributes, we need to first understand how the body functions on a cellular level and the mechanism of cell development, growth, differentiation and finally cell multiplication.

Causes of cancer – the how

As we have seen, once in a while the body's amazing system malfunctions and a cell starts multiplying more than necessary or inappropriately, giving rise to abnormal cells unable to perform useful functions. The immune system usually manages to destroy such cells before they present any real threat to the organism.

If an abnormal cell escapes immune system surveillance and survives, it may start behaving of its own accord (*autonomy*), and replicate itself to form multiple disobedient cells. Such cells, by virtue of their abnormal DNA, lose their normal differentiation and their orientation to one another and to their surrounding framework (*anaplasia*). They are able to multiply very rapidly and as they do not listen to any laws laid down by the constitution of the organism – the normal DNA – they can spread wildly in all directions, invading the surrounding tissues or spreading to distant tissues (*metastasis*).

Generally, normal cells have an inbuilt genetic coding which can initiate steps to induce cell death when appropriate

19

(*apoptosis*). In malignant cells this inbuilt safety mechanism becomes dysfunctional. In addition, there are mechanisms by which the normal cell keeps checking and repairing the DNA content. These are also bypassed in these malignant cells, giving rise to a cancerous DNA structure. Cancerous cells also have a tendency to consume much larger amounts of glucose than normal cells and to rely on inefficient methods of producing ATP.

Cancer, as we have seen, can arise in virtually any of the body's cell types. There are certain genetic mutations that take place in the DNA of the cell, resulting in faulty cell multiplication. This leads to the development of cells which have behaviour vastly different to normal cells. These new cells display autonomy, anaplasia and often metastasis, loss of apoptosis and use relatively large amounts of glucose. They thus act as parasites within the body, growing at the cost of other cells.

The fact that cancer cells grow without the normal control mechanisms leads to the formation of tumours. Tumours grow in a series of steps. The first step is often *hyperplasia*, excessive and uncontrolled growth of cells due to uncontrolled cell division. These cells appear normal, but changes have occurred that result in *some* loss of control over their growth.

Fig. 3.1: Steps of Cancer Formation

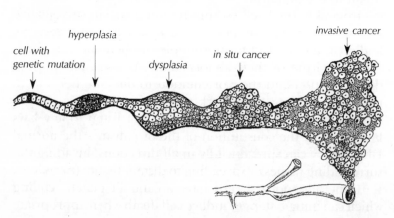

cell with genetic mutation

hyperplasia

dysplasia

in situ cancer

invasive cancer

The second step is *dysplasia*, resulting from further growth, accompanied by abnormal changes to the cells. The functionality of the cells undergoes damage, unlike in hyperplasia where the cells continue to function normally. It should be noted that dysplasia does not necessarily progress to cancer.

In certain tissues, lesions called *carcinoma in situ* may arise. These refer to a condition in which dysplastic changes are severe and involve an extensive amount of tissue. These lesions are considered to be pre-invasive or pre-cancerous.

At this stage, because the tumour is still contained within its original location (called *in situ*) and is not invasive, it is not considered malignant, but it is potentially malignant. Invasive cancer may subsequently develop.

Cancers may also metastasize, that is, spread from the original site to another part of the body. Cancer cells metastasize by spreading via lymphatic and blood vessels to distant sites. Thankfully, not all cancers progress to this point.

Angiogenesis in tumour cells

Angiogenesis means the formation of new blood vessels. This happens normally, as in wound healing, and is also an important part of cancer growth. Without the additional blood supplied by angiogenesis, cancers can grow no larger than one or two millimetres.

Although cancer cells are no longer dependent on the control mechanisms that govern normal cells, they still require nutrients, including oxygen, in order to grow. Virtually all living tissues are amply supplied with capillaries (tiny blood vessels), which bring nutrients and oxygen to, and remove waste from, every cell. As cancerous tumours enlarge, not all cells can be supplied by the normal blood vessels. To provide a blood supply for all the cells in the tumour, it must rely on new blood vessels.

Under normal circumstances, when new blood vessel formation is required, 'activator chemicals' are released by the body. When cells in the existing blood vessels are exposed to these chemicals, they grow and divide, producing new blood vessels. Cancer cells produce these activator chemicals, which signal to the blood vessels in the surrounding normal tissue and encourage the growth of new blood vessels. Angiogenic cells, which can trigger the production of new blood vessels to feed the cancerous growth, facilitate rapid growth of the tumour. Cancer-causing genes (oncogenes) in the DNA of cancer cells increase the production of the activator chemicals that trigger angiogenesis.

When cancerous cells start this autonomous, uncontrolled production of activator chemicals, the result is the formation of new blood vessels which are suited to the requirements of the cancer and not to the entire organism.

Risk factors for cancer

The following table gives a partial list of factors considered to be implicated in the cancerous transformation of cells.

Table 3.1: Cancer: Risk Factors*

Tobacco	Both active and passive smoking, and chewing.
Dietary excesses and certain food chemicals	i) excess fats ii) heterocyclic amines (found in meat, especially when cooked at high temperatures such as fried and barbecued) iii) acrylamide (high levels found in potato chips and other foods cooked at high temperatures) iv) being overweight v) pickled and salt-preserved foods vi) soy – high levels could increase risk of oestrogen-responsive cancers such as breast and uterine cancers vii) sugar – through obesity link viii) trans-saturated fats – possible link (all fats have a link with obesity) ix) Vitamin A – excessive doses (as in too many supplements) may increase lung cancer risk

Malnutrition	*i) deficient fibre* *ii) deficiencies of anti-oxidant micro-nutrients such as certain vitamins* *iii) deficiencies of minerals like magnesium and selenium*
Occupational materials	*asbestos, benzene, benzedrine and formaldehyde (used in industrial manufacture), vinyl chloride (plastic manufacture)*
Pollution	*including certain pesticides and some heavy metals*
Sunlight	*excess sunlight/UV radiation*
Ionizing radiation	*x-rays, nuclear fallout*
Certain pharmaceutical drugs	*hormone replacement therapy may increase the risk of some cancers; some drugs used to treat cancer are associated with a risk of cancer developing in other parts of the body*
Alcohol	
Some viruses and bacteria	*including human papilloma virus, hepatitis B and C, helicobacter pylori, human immunodeficiency virus*
Age	*advancing age*
Psychological influences	*some studies show suppression of negative emotions and feelings of helplessness are linked to the spread and growth of cancer. According to studies so far, there is a stronger association between psychological stress and the spread of cancer than the initial development of cancer* [1, 2]
Repeated trauma	*e.g. long term scratching of a spot so that it cannot heal can lead to the site transforming into certain types of skin cancer*
Genetics	*some cancers are linked to inherited genetic mutations. Most cancers do not run in families*

*Not all of the factors listed apply to all types of cancer.

Having thus understood the basics of normal cells, the amazing body, a simplified mechanism of cancer formation and having some idea of some of the key risk factors causing cancer, let us go on to analyze the exact cell growth mechanism of these cancerous cells.

4

The Molecular Basis of Cancer Development

Non-lethal genetic damage lies at the heart of the development of cancer (carcinogenesis). Abnormalities may be acquired by damage to the cell from environmental factors, dietary factors or lifestyle factors or can be inherited. The development of cancer occurs in stages. It takes place at the DNA level, which is situated within the nucleus of each cell and manifests in the physical body level. The genetic code represents the potential manifestation and is known as the *genotype*. The *phenotype* is the body's final physical manifestation of the genetic code.

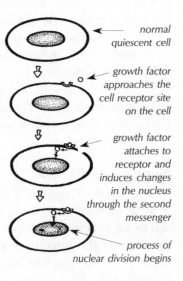

normal quiescent cell

growth factor approaches the cell receptor site on the cell

growth factor attaches to receptor and induces changes in the nucleus through the second messenger

process of nuclear division begins

Fig. 4.1

The genotype's expression in the phenotype may be altered by lifestyle, occupation, pollution and possibly by emotions, behaviour, habits, personality patterns and even by certain thought patterns (provided they are powerful and focused enough). These factors may either encourage or inhibit the expression of certain gene structures which play a role in gene expression or activation and thereby play a role

25

either directly or indirectly in carcinogenesis. For example, a person might have genes predisposing them to angina and heart attack, but if the lifestyle, climate, diet and emotional state are healthy, then the chance of this disease manifesting in the physical body is greatly reduced and if the disease manifests at all, its severity is minimized. An unhealthy combination of all these subsidiary factors in the presence of a disease predisposing gene or genes greatly increases the chances of manifestation of cancer at the physical level.

This would be the reason why a lifelong chain smoker does not get lung cancer, while a total abstainer from cigarettes develops the disease. More detailed analysis would likely show that in the case of this particular smoker, the sum total of the predisposing and protective factors was protective. His smoking, which greatly predisposed him to cancer, was nullified by protective factors. The abstainer did not smoke, but other factors in his life might have been strongly predisposing to cancer and so it manifested in him. These predisposing and protective factors are mysterious and not fully understood.

Normal cell division

The process of normal cell division is initiated by specific growth factors. Growth factors instigate changes inside the cell by stimulating a specific *receptor* (signal-receiving structure) present on the outside of the cell. These changes are then carried to the nucleus of the cell wherein corresponding changes take place causing the cell to undergo division and multiplication. Ordinary multiplication is also known as *mitosis*. It is a process in which DNA duplicates itself to form two identical sets of DNA, followed by cell division to finally form two new and genetically identical cells (see Fig. 4.2).

There are two sets of regulatory genes: tumour-promoting oncogenes and tumour-inhibiting *cancer suppressor genes*. Cancer-suppressor genes, if damaged, lose their ability to regulate cell growth in such a way as to protect against malignant change. *Oncogenes* arise from a mutation of normal

26

Fig. 4.2: Normal Cell Division

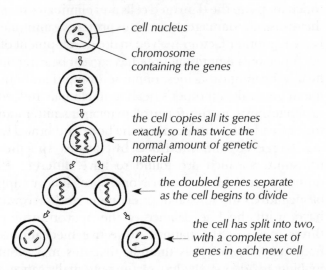

cell nucleus

chromosome containing the genes

the cell copies all its genes exactly so it has twice the normal amount of genetic material

the doubled genes separate as the cell begins to divide

the cell has split into two, with a complete set of genes in each new cell

gene, known as proto-oncogenes. Proto-oncogenes code for proteins involved in normal cell growth and division. Oncogenes code for abnormal, cancer-causing cell growth proteins, which do not obey the usual inactivation methods of the cells. By coding for abnormal versions (or quantities) of growth-control proteins, oncogenes trigger uncontrolled and overactive cell growth by multiple mechanisms. A cancer cell may contain one or more oncogenes, which means that one or more aspects of cell growth will be abnormal.

Such uncontrolled and overactive cell growth is one step towards manifestation of malignancy in the body. Each such step needs to be complemented by other similarly carcinogenic transformations to develop a cancer. An accumulation of multiple such changes causes the actual physical manifestation of cancer in the body. Every human cancer that has been analyzed reveals multiple genetic alterations involving the activation of more than one oncogene and a loss of two or more cancer suppressor genes.

It can be a surprising discovery that the process of potentially carcinogenic transformation in the body happens frequently. However, there is a part of our immune system which mops up the damaged cells and eliminates them before they cause any damage. Loss of this protective immune surveillance is another factor involved in the development of cancer.

A person's emotional state has a great bearing on overall health, healing capacities, immune strength and outlook on life in general. A mother's healing touch may indeed have a concrete basis in the form of neurotransmitters and their widespread action throughout the body and brain. Emotions are triggered and modified by various specific neurotransmitters which are found to have different effects in different parts of the body. Non-expression or suppression of 'negative emotions' like grief, anger and sorrow can play havoc with the fine balance of the neurotransmitters and throw many of the natural protective mechanisms in the body out of gear. It is thought that this may result in an inability to adequately destroy the potentially cancerous cells mentioned above, leading to cancer.

Thus we see that the development of cancer is a multi-step genetic process triggered off by various risk factors. These factors can have a direct, indirect or contributory role to play in the degradation of a normal cell to a cancer cell. If some of the steps of cancer formation (i.e. progressive cellular damage from hyperplasia, dysplasia, etc.) become blocked at any one or more levels, the degradation of a cell to a cancer cell halts at that level. This need for *multiple* genetic alterations is the weakest link in the development of cancer. General factors like diet, the immune system and emotional wellbeing can also play a role in cellular damage or its prevention by virtue of their effects on the cells at neurotransmitter levels.

Where cancer strikes and how it spreads

Cancer is a disease which can strike anywhere in the body. It can be characterized first by the type of cell which it affects and then according to the location where it affects the body.

Malignancies affecting the epithelium (cellular covering of internal and external body surfaces, e.g. the lining of the digestive tract and the skin) are generally known as *carcinomas*, and malignancies affecting the muscles, blood vessels and connective tissue are generally known as *sarcomas*. Cancers arising from bone marrow cells are known as *lymphomas* and those affecting white blood cells are termed *leukaemias*.

Malignancies spread by various mechanisms. The most common methods are local invasion, through the lymphatic system, or via the bloodstream. Medical procedures (such as when a needle is inserted into a cancer for diagnostic purposes and then withdrawn through normal tissue) may theoretically also cause spread. Each malignancy usually follows a characteristic mode of spread, although it can be modified by other factors, such as age.

The lymphatic system is an auxiliary system which functions along with the circulatory system to bring fluid from the body tissues back into the bloodstream. The blood follows a specific course of circulation to carry oxygen from the lungs to the tissues of the body and remove carbon dioxide and metabolic waste products from the tissues of the body. Blood returns (via venules and veins) to the lungs for the exchange of carbon dioxide and oxygen. Other waste products are dealt with by the kidneys and the liver.

In the course of circulation, the blood reaches the tissue via the arteries, arterioles and capillaries. At the tissue level, excess water and proteins leak out from the blood vessels into the tissues, bathing the cells and carrying various nutrients needed by the tissues. This fluid needs to be removed, otherwise swelling will develop. The fluid moves from the tissues into tiny lymphatic capillaries, where it is called 'lymph'. These lymphatic capillaries are tributaries of larger lymphatic vessels which ultimately drain into a vein in the chest region.

This lymphatic fluid is filtered at various points along its pathway with the aim of eliminating any germs, toxins or other harmful products, so that the lymph which thus enters the blood is free from any noxious material. This job of filtering and elimination is done by the lymph nodes, other

29

lymphatic glands (such as the tonsils) and the spleen. Lymph nodes and the lymph itself contain specialized cells known as lymphocytes which can actively kill much foreign material. The lymph nodes filter the malignant cells, which detach themselves from the local site of the malignancy and travel along the lymphatic channels to spread through the body. Lymph nodes are therefore often the first site to which cancer cells spread from their original position. While certain cancers have characteristic places to which they metastasize, it is difficult to predict whether a given cancer will spread via lymphatic or bloodstream channels.

It is worth noting at this stage that these malignant cells in the body derive their nutrition and requirements from the body itself, meaning that they start acting like parasites and grow rapidly at the cost of the neighbouring tissues. To support themselves, they need more blood supply and other hormonal requirements for cell division and growth. As we have seen, they achieve this by initiating a series of new blood vessels. At times they also start producing certain hormones necessary for cancer growth and maintenance. Thus, a cancer originating in one part of the body can spread to adjacent areas as well as to very distant and apparently unrelated organs of the body. This compounds the issue of managing the cancer as well as its debilitating effects on the body and mind.

5

Nutrition and its Role in Cancer

The human body, capable of performing the most amazing feats, possessed of unbelievable capacities, survival skills, versatility and adaptability, is made up of four basic structures or macronutrients. These are the proteins, carbohydrates, fats and water. The body also needs many other micronutrients (vitamins and minerals) in order to carry out its normal functions. A deficiency in any of these vital constituents results in many diseases and disorders. Extensive discussion of these nutrients, their minimum and optimal recommended daily dosages, their role in positive health and their sources can be found in books specializing in this subject. Here, we will touch briefly on this topic for the purpose of looking at the role of nutrition in cancer management.

The journey of life begins when we receive DNA from our parents and nutrients from our mother. The scriptures describe this beautifully as the mother providing the field and the father the seed, so that the sapling of life can blossom. The DNA needs raw material in the form of proteins, carbohydrates, fats, water and a host of other micronutrients like vitamins, minerals and so on to manifest the blueprint coded within itself. For the first nine months, the mother provides these to the growing foetus through a complex structure known as the placenta. After birth, the individual has to gradually and increasingly take responsibility for providing these. This is, of course, accomplished

31

through the food we eat, the water we drink and the air we breathe.

The food we eat is broken down into its basic components. Proteins are broken down into amino acids (of which there are a total of 20), the basic structure of proteins. Nine amino acids are 'essential', the other eleven can be formed from the essential nine. Carbohydrates and fats are broken down into smaller compounds (such as glucose and fatty acids) and these are then absorbed from the digestive tract and distributed around the body. The liver is the metabolic epicentre of the body, converting the absorbed nutrients into usable substances and storing them until needed. Directed by the blueprint (the DNA) and modified by feedback from the body, the liver assimilates the amino acids, glucose and fat derivatives into various types of proteins, carbohydrates and fats. When appropriate, recipient cells and tissues absorb and use them for energy or to form structures of varying degrees of specialization, such as cell membranes, lung tissue, the brain, eye and ear structures. Indeed, each and every cell and structure of the body is formed from the ingested material.

Anabolism, catabolism and metabolism

The process of assimilation of nutrients and the formation of various complex structural units is known as *anabolism*, while the breakdown of nutrients is known as *catabolism*. The entire activity is known as *metabolism*. Metabolism uses extremely complex chemical reactions in the formation of the final products (for use in the body) and their subsequent breakdown and removal from the body in the form of detoxification. To be able to perform all these tasks successfully, the body has developed special means in the form of highly specialized organelles within the cell. They perform these activities by a series of extremely complex and complicated chemical reactions which employ a series of enzymes and metabolic pathway chains to achieve their results. Most of these reactions take place in an important sub-cellular organelle called the *mitochondria*, present in all cells. The greater the metabolic requirement of the cell, the higher the number of mito-chondria present in that particular type of cell.

Disease formation and progression in the body occurs when the nutrients provided to the body are deficient, inadequate or if the metabolic processes are disturbed so that cellular activities are hampered. Changes in the internal environment of the cell can have some bearing on the ability to withstand, prevent and correct the carcinogenic changes taking place in the body due to various cancer promoting factors. Many such food items change the cellular environment and cause modifications in their behaviour, and hence have come to be called *behaviour response modifiers* (BRMs). Some BRMs also cause genetic change. Hence, such items are now termed carcinogens. It is in our interest to avoid carcinogenic foods.

There is another class of food which induces beneficial changes in the body and neutralizes pro-carcinogenic activity. It does this by various mechanisms, including improving cellular capacity by modifying the cellular environment and enhancing the cell immune capacity. It goes without saying that we need to increase such food items in our diet so as to maintain a healthy internal cellular environment in the body. Thus we have different types and qualities of food – the raw material from which the entire body is created and maintained.

If the quality of raw material supplied is poor, the body tries to supplement the deficiency from its own reserves. If this does not suffice, it starts rationing by supplying the building blocks to those systems essential for survival and reducing the supply to other systems. This results in reduced efficiency in the various skilled activities that we carry out. There is a world of difference between surviving and thriving. If there is malnutrition, the quality of the various body structures that are produced starts diminishing, and this can lead to defects and disorders manifesting in ways such as fatigue, a sense of unwellness (malaise), reduced work efficiency and finally structural disturbances and disease states which are initially reversible and later become permanent.

Familiar examples are vitamin D deficiency causing rickets and vitamin C deficiency causing scurvy.

In addition to this slow, inexorable progression of disease, there is yet another facet of the disease process in the body. The raw materials taken in (food, water and air) may be sufficient, but may have additional components which are directly harmful. The problems are much more dramatic and potentially lethal in such cases. For example, it takes just a few milligrams of cyanide to irreversibly paralyze the entire body within minutes so that survival becomes impossible. The same is the case with poisons containing curare, which leads to paralysis of the breathing musculature. While these chemicals cause immediate and extreme harm, certain food products can act insidiously over a number of years before their harmful effects become apparent.

We are what we eat. We are already aware of this fact, and whether we choose to ignore it or acknowledge it makes or mars our life in the long run. Certain foods may help reduce the risk of cancer and it would seem wise to include them in our diet. On the other hand, it seems sensible to avoid potentially carcinogenic foodstuffs as these might aggravate any predisposition. The link between diet and cancer is currently the focus of much research.

Nourishing the mind
In addition to the physical aspect of nourishment, eating has a powerful psychological link. Eating, the process of acquiring nourishment, is essential for the survival of the body and as such is intimately associated with strong emotions. Hunger is one of the strongest basic instincts and a driving force in life. The thoughts and emotions associated with eating have a direct impact on the psyche, which is reflected in a person's attitude and behaviour. These impressions go into the mix that moulds the personality of each individual. When inappropriately expressed, they can cause a range of behavioural abnormalities and even diseases. This effect highlights the importance of maintaining a positive mental and emotional

state during eating. It should be remembered that this also applies to the experience of being nourished from earliest infancy through childhood when it is the duty of the parents and carers to ensure that feeding and mealtimes are not associated with stress or distress.

Swami Satyananda has said, "Just as food is nourishment for the body, thoughts are nourishment for the mind." Many people take care to maintain proper nutrition through diets, vitamins pills and supplements. Yet do we pause to think about the nourishment of the mind? If the mind is malnourished, it will be unable to withstand the rigours of life, just as a malnourished body cannot defend itself against disease. The ups and downs of life can easily break the mind, sinking it into despondency and gloom. Self doubt, despair and depressive tendencies are all symptoms of a mal-nourished, and therefore weakened, mind.

The mind constantly receives inputs from the outside world through the senses. Events, circumstances and training mould the perception and cognition of the mind. If the mind is continually exposed to negative, self-destructive and brooding tendencies, it responds accordingly. These weaken the mind so that it loses its ability to successfully steer the chariot of life. Even a single, powerful, negative or over-whelming situation can be enough to set off a string of negative thoughts and emotions which can finally result in disease and disorder.

Did not even the legendary warrior prince Arjuna, of the Indian spiritual epic, the *Mahabharata,* face a situation of this type? All his life he had prepared to battle his cousins, the Kauravas. On the brink of the final declaration of the long-awaited, inevitable war, his mind became totally overwhelmed at the possibly disastrous consequences. To fight or not to fight became the all-consuming question. He was able to turn to Lord Krishna, who inspired him and effectively nullified his vicious self-doubting, depressive thought patterns and gave him positive thought processes, enabling him to lift his mind from the depths of despair. Emerging victorious

35

from his internal war with the mind, Arjuna was able to engage single-mindedly in the external war. This story from the *Bhagavad Gita* teaches us how to approach life and successfully tame the mind. It also shows that the company of the wise and maintaining contact with their thought processes and positive spirit is a safety net when the mind is thrown off balance. Such beings nourish and strengthen the mind.

Diet

Cancer, as we have seen, is the result of multi-step cellular dysfunction. Studies have now shown that some dietary items and cooking methods (see chapter 3 and below) contain or produce substances which are possibly carcinogenic in nature. Eating such foods may increase the risk of developing cancer.

By contrast, many fresh, unprocessed fruits and vegetables and some other foods have been shown to contain a number of antioxidants and other substances which are thought to possess anti-carcinogenic properties. It is in our interests to include such items in our diet. These antioxidants have been shown to even inhibit the growth of cells in which cancerous transformation has already taken place. It should be noted that as well as being present in fruits and vegetables, antioxidants are found in some meat, poultry and fish.

In summary, diet has a strong bearing on health and disease in human beings. The risk of cancer, caused by genetic damage to cells, may be reduced, and some say the disease itself may even be reversed, by maintaining an optimal health-promoting diet. In addition, eating also has a strong psychic component which can play a pivotal role in the management of cancer. Finally, nourishment is not limited to the food eaten for the physical body. Thoughts are food for the mind, spirit or psyche and the positive health of the mind and psyche is of utmost importance in maintaining health. Positive thoughts, attitude and mental patterns go a long way in breaking the self-defeating brooding mechanisms of the mind which, according to yoga, can act as a powerful mental carcinogen. Hence, a diet which nourishes all these components needs to be adopted for successful management of cancer.

The American Cancer Society (ACS) gives seven dietary suggestions for the general population:
1. Avoid obesity
2. Cut down on total fat intake
3. Eat more high-fibre foods, including whole grains, fruits, and vegetables
4. Include cruciferous vegetables, such as cauliflower, broccoli, and cabbage
5. Include foods rich in vitamins A and C
6. Lower alcohol consumption
7. Lower intake of salt-cured, smoked, or nitrite-containing foods.

Table 5.1: Cancer Prevention: Dietary Suggestions

Foods having a beneficial role in cancer prevention (organic if possible)	
Cruciferous vegetables	e.g. cabbage, broccoli, cauliflower
Other vegetables	particularly those containing lycopene (tomatoes, watermelon)
Whole grains and other high-fibre foods	
Fruits	
Poultry	
Fish	untreated, smaller fish that are low in the food chain
Legumes	
Some nuts and seeds	
Seaweeds/sea vegetables	
Foods high in calcium	(not calcium supplements) may reduce bowel cancer risk
Foods high in folate	
Garlic	some sources say garlic may reduce risk of some types of cancer
Water	plenty of water may reduce risk of bladder cancer

6

Stress and Cancer

In physics, the concept of stress is explained as the ability of an object to withstand an external deforming force. For example, if a block of concrete is subjected to a crushing force, the molecules of the block exert an equal and opposing force from within to counteract and nullify this external force. Depending upon the capacity of the block of concrete and its innate structural strength, this internal force increases in direct proportion to the external force, until the threshold level is reached. If the external force increases beyond this, the block of concrete develops cracks and will be crushed. Frequent application of similar multiple stressors hastens the wear and tear of the block of concrete, wearing it down.

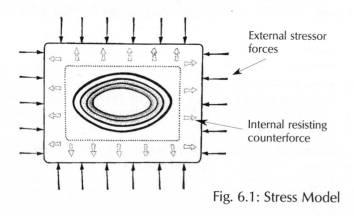

External stressor forces

Internal resisting counterforce

Fig. 6.1: Stress Model

Humans and stress

Stress has a similar effect on living beings. However, many more factors come into play due to the fact that humans are capable of repair and regeneration, as well as having the ability to adjust, adapt and modify themselves and their responses to the stressors. Stress in humans can be defined as an event or a circumstance (either external or internal), which exerts a potentially deforming force on the internal environment in the body-mind. The individual responds to these stressor forces and carries out specific activities in an effort to maintain homeostasis (constancy of the internal environment). Stressors and their responses can be classified as being externalized, i.e. projected into the external manifest world, or as internalized, i.e. operating on the internal mental and psychic plane.

In non-living objects, such as the block of concrete in the above example, there is no scope for improvement and modification once the concrete block is cast. The molecules have a fixed maximum threshold up to which they can respond without any adverse effect. In living beings, however, the ability to respond is not fixed. It is dynamic in nature and hence can adjust and adapt. Exposure to the stressor can therefore become a way of strengthening the individual as expressed in the saying, 'tempered by experience'. As long as there are no longterm adverse effects on the body-mind, the stressor can be beneficial as it helps the individual to mature and grow in their capacity to manage life. Such stressors are then said to be character building – eustress. When the force exceeds the maximum 'eu-response' levels, the impact on the body and mind becomes progressively adverse, resulting in disease and degeneration – distress.

Stressors can be classified as:
- Dietary/nutritional
- Occupational
- Interpersonal
- Mental
- Disease processes
- Environmental.

These are cumulative in nature and when added up can significantly reduce the capacity of the individual to face disease and to overcome it.

Stressors act by instigating a series of neurohormonal changes in the brain and body. As a result various hormones are secreted which bring about behavioural changes in the body. At the same time, the brain function also changes and it starts directing the body to act in a different manner (depending upon the nature of the stressor, etc.). External and internal stressors operate in the same manner, which means that for purposes of cognition and response there is no essential difference between them. The mind responds in exactly the same way to an external stressor force (objective reality) as it does to the stressor force arising from thoughts and images in the mind (subjective reality). The degree of threat perceived in both cases is indistinguishable. The same neurotransmitters are involved in a coordinated sequence of responses from the body-mind. These neurotransmitters jumpstart coordinated sequences of responses from various body systems in order to ward off the stressor stimuli and maintain internal homeostasis (Pert, 2003)[3]. The well-known 'fight or flight' reflex is just one of the many mechanisms operating in the body for this purpose.

The result of stressful stimuli can be summarized as:

1. Stimulation of the immune system: a high alert is sounded and the immune cells act as if a foreign body (equivalent to a threat to physical existence) has entered the body and prepare to fight it. However, with long term stress, the immune system is actually weakened.
2. Increased sympathetic nervous system activity involving the whole body.
3. A state of hyperarousal in the neural pathways, leading to an increase in aggressive tendencies.
4. Release of brain chemicals and hormones that lead to an increase in blood glucose.
5. Increase in the metabolic rate and cell repair and regeneration mechanism.

A stressor acts upon the body-mind apparatus and extracts a response. The body learns from this experience – a memory of the event is created and stored in the mental hard disk where it can be referenced for further use. This event has a bearing on the response of the individual should a similar event occur. When the same stimulus (or a stimulus that the body-mind associates with this event) occurs again, the body-mind is thus primed for a response. The body-mind can become conditioned to produce a particular response to a given stressor.

In this way, over a period of time, associations are formed and can result in an almost involuntary, automated response to the same event or to any stimulus perceived by the mind to be associated with that event. Even if the specific response is no longer appropriate, the automation continues and almost 'forces' the individual to respond in the same manner. A simple example would be the inordinate fear of darkness in some individuals, or the inability of a fully grown elephant to snap a thin piece of string tying its knees together because it still remembers the futility of the effort it had made to break free from the string as a small baby. Many phobias and obsessions can be traced to this phenomenon. This now inappropriate response results in many of the ill effects of stress.

Such stressors cause a specific biochemical sequence of events to occur inside the body in order to elicit the necessary response. Repeated and continual stressful events leave the body-mind in a perpetually alert state and result in the repeated expression of particular genes associated with the stress response. The genes orchestrate each event in the body by processing and forming specific, appropriate proteins, e.g. enzymes or hormones.

It is thought that stressful stimuli also affect, at a molecular level, the supporting structure of the DNA. These changes are described as 'epigenetic.' *Science Update* (May, 2008)[4] states: "Unlike mutations, epigenetic changes are not variations in the sequences of building blocks that make up the DNA in a gene. The genes remain stable, but environmental factors, such as stress, diet and maternal care received early in life, act on the supporting structures of DNA, causing the DNA code that comprises a gene to be exposed for longer or shorter periods of time, essentially turning the gene on or off, and allowing it to produce more or less protein. This change in protein production, in turn, can affect physical and behavioral traits, and can be passed on from one cell to the next as they multiply within an organism, and even from parents to children."

Cellular memory is transmitted across generations of cells in the genetic material that the mother cell transmits to the daughter cell. It seems that these stimuli affect supporting structures of the DNA and possibly predispose the daughter cell to respond in the same manner as the mother cell had a long time ago, even if the external situation has changed considerably. The body then has to relearn and modify its genetic memory to suit the new environmental conditions. This implies genetic modification in order to realign the genetic memory with the new circumstance.

Many lifestyle events now considered by the intellect to be normal are still recognized by body mechanisms as threatening because the definitions of threat and response are still basically primitive. Hence, a television serial or music considered by a teenager to be stimulating and fun might be perceived by the body as a threat and become a stressor. The accumulated effect of such stressors is a frenzy of body-mind activity, and hence of certain genetic activity also.

It is postulated that this situation predisposes the DNA to instability and genetic mutations. These mutations might be beneficial, but may also result in carcinogenic changes. Chronic stress also weakens the immune system, and the immune system is important in preventing cancer. In such circumstances, cancer may result even if there are no physical carcinogens present.

Stress and cancer
Stress is an important evolutionary force in the life of an individual, providing opportunities to expand one's capacity

to deal with life at the physical level as well as on the mental and emotional levels. For this to happen, however, there needs to be appropriate spacing of the stressor stimuli so that the shortcomings exposed by each stimulus can be examined, analyzed and worked upon. This is a process of assimilation, regeneration and growth. This process is maximized when there is a balanced attitude towards the situation and the person is able to make the mental effort at introspection. This enables reaching an understanding of the situation in its entirety, rather than reacting according to preconceived notions or someone else's advice. Finally, the most important aspect of responding to the stressor stimuli is implementation of the decision that has been arrived at. This action needs to take place to complete the chain of events.

Of course, life is not lived in laboratory conditions, but ideally there is a minimal critical gap between the two consecutive stressful stimuli to allow the person time to experience positive growth-promoting 'adaptive-stress' rather than harmful 'di-stress'. Occurrence of multiple stressors too close to each other can result in the system malfunctioning.

As we have seen, carcinogenesis occurs due to genetic mutations which transform normal cells into cancerous cells. The *possible* mechanisms of the contributory effect of stress in carcinogenesis are briefly outlined below.

1. Exposure to recurrent episodes of stress (of varied origins) induces specific patterns of cellular activity so that specific protein molecules needed to respond to the stress are produced. This may cause changes to the supporting structures of DNA, and possibly erroneous copies to be made. Some of these variations could give rise to genes with oncogenic potential and may also affect the cancer suppressor genes present in the gene bank. As seen earlier, activation of oncogenes and/or inactivation of cancer suppressor genes are implicated in beginning the process of cancerous transformation.

2. The body's responses to the stressors are very simple. For the body, the stressor stimulus is a threat to survival.

Ensuring survival is the highest priority and the body has many emergency responses that it activates to achieve this purpose. It is akin to defending a country against invading enemy forces – a do or die situation. At these times, it is suggested that the body's normal 'checking' circuits may be bypassed to achieve immediate survival. This bypassing could create a loophole through which genetic mutations are tolerated by the body.

One hypothesis states that chronic 'stress response' by the body creates an environment where the body is in a state of continual stimulation and emergency, maintaining itself through the emergency responses to allow its emergency services to successfully neutralize the danger or 'threat to survival'. It is postulated by some that in the presence of other carcinogenic factors, these conditions predispose carcinogenesis (Day, 2005)[5] .

Stress and the hormones released by the body to quell the stress have a blunting effect on the immune system as far as cancer surveillance and clean up is concerned. White cell numbers increase during short term stress, but long term stress weakens the immune system. This proves to be a shot in the arm for the cancer cells. They opportunistically take advantage of the chance to progress and multiply with minimal resistance to their activity, and in this way the cancerous process can take root in the body.

3. Stressful situations are fraught with extremely powerful emotional stimuli and can bring up a host of feelings within. Not all of the feelings are considered appropriate and as such may be suppressed. Emotions and thought patterns have corresponding neuropeptides in the body-mind. Ongoing emotional trauma or painful memories will cause neuropeptides to be produced. These neuropeptides continue to cause stress for the whole organism.

All these and other mechanisms have a cumulative effect on the body-mind. Over a period of time, it is postulated that they build up, creating a strong predisposition towards cancerous transformation. Stress, the bane of modern civilization and lifestyles, can thus strike us from within. Preventing, minimizing and controlling/managing as many of these mechanisms can, logically, help avert cancer.

The crucial question is how to do it. There are many ways to counter stress. Yoga has been shown to be one of the most effective, harmonious and simple strategies to counter stress. As bringing about all the required changes is an arduous task, an integrated approach of yoga and conventional medications can be adopted. This combination can work wonders in managing cancer. The medications take care of the present tumour, while yoga as a lifestyle may help prevent further occurrences and assist conventional therapies in managing the tumour.

It should be noted that from an academic viewpoint, evidence is lacking about the complex relationship between cancer and stress. Scientists know that psychological stress alone can affect the immune system, which as we have seen is important in the body's defence against cancer. It is also well known that longterm stress increases the risk of obesity, which is another well known risk factor for cancer. Of course, stress also tends to lead to behaviour such as smoking and alcohol abuse which increase the risk of cancer.

Decades of academic studies have examined the relationship between stress and cancer. Some studies have indicated a link between psychological factors and the risk of developing cancer, but a direct cause-and-effect relationship has not been proven. This may be because stress comes in many varieties, as does cancer, making the research more complex.

Research implies that the reduction in immune system activity associated with stress makes cancer more likely. Research on animals also suggests that the release of stress hormones can affect important cellular processes (such as DNA repair) and thus potentially increase the risk of cancer.

Research does seem to suggest that stress plays a role in the growth and spread of a cancer that is already present. Studies suggest an association between feeling helpless and suppressing negative emotions, and the growth or spread of

45

cancer. This relationship was not consistently seen in all studies, and its physiological mechanisms have not been explained in the scientific literature.

However, one thing seems certain: that even though the causative factors may be different in today's times, stress exists in most people with cancer. In fact, the cancer itself poses great stress to the system, not to mention stress due to the mental anguish and turmoil caused by the diagnosis. Stress, especially its di-stress component, brings about many changes in the body which reduce its ability to face the challenges posed by exposure to various cancer risk factors. As such, it seems a prudent move to neutralize the harmful effects of stress on the body-mind-spirit complex, so that it can be in a better position to face the stress posed by these risk factors.

2: How Yoga Practices Work

7

A Fresh Perspective on Cancer Management

Current conventional modes of therapy for cancer

Having analyzed the behaviour of malignant cells and looked at the cellular basis of cancer in Part 1, let us now apply our newfound knowledge. First we will examine current therapy modalities in order to understand the rationale that is followed in attempting to control and eliminate this deadly malfunction.

Cancer poses some unique difficulties for successful treatment. Some of the challenges of cancer management are:
- Unlike other diseases, cancer is not a single entity which can merit a single specific cure.
- It is not caused by an alien agent that can be targeted and eliminated.

Surgical removal of the malignant growth was the first form of cancer therapy. Surgery, radiation and chemotherapy form the mainstay of present cancer therapy.

The spread of cancer has been studied in great detail. For many cancers, much is known about the most effective methods to identify and surgically remove cancerous cells. This is an extremely effective means of stopping the spread of cancer. Surgery involves removal of the original tumour and any secondary lesions. Those lymph nodes into which the tumour mass drains its lymphatic fluids are sometimes removed in case they contain undetected tumour cells.

49

Chemotherapy consists of certain cytotoxic drugs which kill cells that have cancerous attributes. After much research, drugs that attack cancer cells have been developed. These drugs target the cancer cells and use various mechanisms to kill them. Unfortunately, they also kill certain normal cells whose behaviour has characteristics in common with the behaviour of cancer cells. For example, many chemotherapeutic drugs target rapidly multiplying cells. The drugs cannot distinguish between normal cells multiplying rapidly (as needed by the body) and cancer cells multiplying rapidly (not needed by the body). Potential blood cells in the bone marrow have a high rate of cell multiplication, so they are affected. The killing of these blood-forming cells gives rise to horrendous side effects, leaving the body extremely debilitated and the immune system compromised.

In radiotherapy, the affected body part is targeted with radioactive rays. This kills the exposed cells, thereby reducing the cancerous cell mass load. As with chemotherapy, the radiation cannot distinguish between normal cells and abnormal cells. All cells exposed to the ionizing rays are destroyed.

Depending on the cancer and the person's general health, an appropriate treatment plan using one of more of the three methods is advocated.

It is interesting to note here that oncologists speak not in terms of cures and failures, but in terms of *remissions, relapses and five year survival.* Remission means the cancer is seemingly gone. Relapse means it is again evident. Even after the best of treatments where there are no apparent malignant cells left in the body, cancers of almost all types can re-emerge. Hence, it is difficult to state that someone is definitively cured. The term 'five-year survival' is more accurate. In general, if a person has lived for at least five years without suffering a relapse, they can effectively be considered cured.

Why do these relapses happen? Where is the shortcoming? How can it be corrected? To be able to successfully answer these fundamental questions we need to change our perspective and analyze further. There is no doubt that many of these therapies have improved survival rates among people diagnosed with cancer, but they aim only at removing the malignant cells. Even if all the malignant cells have been removed, how can one ensure that the basic process of the conversion of normal cells into malignant cells is halted and reversed? The root cause of transformation into cancerous cells is not addressed in these therapies. This means that at best these treatments are only symptomatic or manifestation-oriented. They do not remove the cause of the malignant malformation.

Using yoga in conjunction with conventional medicine
Yoga blends seamlessly with conventional medications and interventions to help manage cancer. It can aid the effect of conventional treatments by reducing their after effects and bolstering the innate fighting forces of the body at the same time.

The relevant principles of yoga are outlined in following chapters. Ways of applying these principles to the therapeutic needs of cancer and integrating them with the medical approach are then explored. There is no final word on the management of cancer and this book does not pretend to give one. The cure for cancer is a multidimensional and long term effort paralleling the onset of cancer. Yoga, however, does shed light on why cancer occurs, including its possible deeper and more subtle causes. It provides mechanisms, based on natural laws, to prevent these subtle imbalances from manifesting as a malignancy, and also provides possible ways to manage or even reverse a malignancy should it arise. These *do* have an effect as long as the practitioner implements the necessary changes in his or her life.

It is postulated that yoga helps to manage cancer in the following ways:
• Reduces the side effects of chemotherapy, such as fatigue and nausea.
• Helps to manage the emotional roller coaster which the patient experiences during the therapy.

- Enhances the desired effects of conventional treatments, namely, radiotherapy, chemotherapy and surgery.
- Improves healing after radiotherapy and surgery by maximizing blood flow to the affected areas and providing a form of gentle movement that can be used when the person's energy is low.
- Brings about harmony amongst the various metabolic activities in the body and achieves a greater degree of metabolic balance.
- Plays an important role in improving the patient's quality of life.

Theoretical aspects of yogic management

So far in our quest to defeat cancer we have tried to understand the what, the when and the where of the disease, plus the available modalities of treatment. In this part we will attempt to gain an understanding of health management through yoga and how it can be used to manage the disease process of cancer.

Cancer is, as we have already seen, a disease in which the cells of the body are affected. The blueprint of life, the DNA of the cell has been hacked into and the code tampered with. As a result the cells lose their normal structure and function, start multiplying rapidly without a control or stopping mechanism, invade the surrounding normal tissues and convert them into similar cancerous growths. This rapid, uncontrolled growth leads to functional derangement of that particular cell, group of cells, tissue, organ and system, and finally the entire human being. In addition, it also plays havoc with the metabolic, circulatory, immune and nutritional functions in the body.

Advances in modern medicine have helped to develop medicines which target rapidly multiplying cells and exterminate them. Research is underway to streamline the effects of these medicines and also to develop newer targeting mechanisms, which zero in on the cancerous cells only. The situation is similar with the other two major forms of treatment: surgery and radiation therapy.

Though it is heartening to know that we are developing newer and more powerful skills to combat this deadly disease, our efforts are not unlike the naive woodcutter who attempts to remove a tree by chopping off its branches, stem and trunk right down to the ground, obliterating all visible signs of the tree. He congratulates himself on a job well done, only to find that a few months later another tree has shot up in the same place. Confused and angry, he attacks the tree again in the same way as before. This process repeats itself as long as he does not pause to reflect upon the cause of this apparently 'immortal' tree which defies death, time and time again. He needs to dig deeper and deeper below the surface of the earth to the very last roots of the tree and remove them. Only then can he truly succeed in eradicating the tree. Even after that, it is imperative that he watches to see that no seeds remain or are replanted by accident or design, for even a single seed is sufficient for the re-emergence of the entire tree all over again.

The need in relation to cancer is to go deeper into its causes, find out why it happens and remove it from our very existence once and for all. We then need to install mechanisms to prevent the re-entry of such weeds in the garden of life. We have looked at the causative agents of cancer as far as they are known. We have also seen that these causative factors affect the DNA of the cell, causing mutations which result in abnormal growth patterns of the affected cells. Such mutations take place occasionally in the body though on a much smaller scale and are destroyed by the immune system before they can cause harm to the body. What is the basic mechanism behind this? Why is it that some people though routinely exposed to the predisposing factors do not develop any sign of cancer, while others who have never been exposed to any known causative factors suddenly develop the disease?

Is it possible that we need to take a fresh look at the facts? What do we mean when we say that the cancerous process affects us? Does it affect the body alone, or does it affect the mind? Conversely, do the causative factors spring from the physical dimension, or from the mind, or from both, or beyond? The latest research points to the disease process being much beyond the body itself. There are indications that the causation process starts deep within us from the higher levels of existence of the human personality. If so, we must first explore and know what these higher dimensions are, how they function and how we can reach those realms and modify the activities going on there.

Yoga provides a way of approaching these queries. It regards the human personality as being much deeper than just the manifest physical body. Yoga gives us a broader vision of who we are and a framework for developing insight and understanding at deeper levels.

What is yoga?

The origins of yoga can be traced back to a far older and deeper oriental system – that of tantra. From time immemorial, humankind has searched for the source of existence. Ancient seers in India not only dedicated their lives to this quest, but they also developed a systematic and scientific approach towards it. These seers found that human existence is not limited to the physical dimension, but spans much higher and subtler levels of being. They realised that the human being is endowed with five distinct dimensions of existence which they termed the five sheaths or *koshas*. Recognizing the koshas or bodies takes our concept of who we are far beyond the physical. The koshas include: *annamaya kosha* (physical sheath), *pranamaya kosha* (energy sheath), *manomaya kosha* (mental sheath), *vijnanamaya kosha* (wisdom sheath) and *anandamaya kosha* (bliss sheath).

The journey of the seers began with the most manifest and obvious level of existence – our physical body and our external world – that which we experience through the senses. As they proceeded to dissect material existence, they gradually came to a stage wherein they reached the fundamental building blocks of nature – the atom. Yes, these scientists of the hoary past had indeed discovered the atom, as is seen in

54

the atomic theory put forth by Sage Kanad. To their dismay, however, they found that the source of life is beyond even the atom and sub-atomic particles, nature's minutest building blocks.

Their search finally led them to discover that the source of life and the higher dimensions of human existence are present not outside the physical being but hidden deep within. To continue this voyage of discovery, they needed to leave behind the senses which had aided them until now, to transcend them and use another set of organs of perception. The senses of touch, taste, smell, sight and hearing help us in our lives on the external plane, but are of no use in our journey to inner planes. They need to be left behind and newer faculties and tools developed to experience these inner dimensions. This is an arduous and difficult task, requiring a great deal of discipline and training. The seers explored various means of accomplishing their aims. Gradually a distillation of knowledge took place and they formulated techniques which enable a person to experience these sheaths and finally transcend them to experience the fountain source of life, known as the soul, or the *atman*.

Yoga's origins are in the distillations of these experiences. The various schools of yoga, such as hatha yoga, raja yoga, bhakti yoga, karma yoga or kriya yoga, are but different approaches systematized over many millennia to suit people's varying psychological frameworks.

The aim of yoga is to experience the subtler aspects of the human personality. Once these subtle aspects are accessed, they are trained and disciplined so that they can be utilized for the expansion of consciousness, ultimately taking us to the point of realization that this individual self is nothing but an extension of the cosmic self or cosmic consciousness. Each dimension of our personality needs to be toned and tuned for maximum performance. To do this, the latent potential of the human personality must be developed. The ancient scientists devised many practices to this end. Our present awareness limits itself to the partial level of the physical dimension and some superficial aspects of the mental dimension. Even here, there are many imbalances, causing hindrances in the development of the complete potential of even the physical dimensions. Yogic practices systematically help in overcoming these obstacles and refining our awareness.

The World Health Organization now defines health as: "A state of complete physical, mental and social wellbeing allowing us to lead a socially and economically productive life, not just absence of disease or infirmity." It speaks of health as being multidimensional, having physical, mental, social, spiritual, emotional, vocational and other dimensions, all of which are closely interrelated. Thus, their vision of positive health has strong parallels with the yogic definition of human life and its aim of realizing the complete potential inherent within. Yogic practices help to improve the quality of each of these dimensions as they have the ability to bring about both qualitative and quantitative change in the basic mechanism of functioning of the human being.

Yogic health management uses yogic practices so that the physical, mental, emotional and psychic aspects of the human being are serviced thoroughly and any shortcomings or system errors which lead to malfunctioning of the entire system and potentially to disease are reversed, corrected and prevented. There is no doubt that achieving this requires hard work, perseverance and dedication. It is not as easy as popping a pill, but the results are deeper and broader.

Understanding and inculcating yogic principles in modern day-to-day life requires an abundance of common sense so that we can differentiate between the essence, which should not be changed, and the accessories, which can shift with the times, circumstances and requirements. This can only be achieved through proper study *and* practice of the science of yoga. Study helps the student gain understanding of the concepts, but it is the experience which teaches much more. The saying 'a ton of theory is worth an ounce of practice' is fully applicable here.

8

Applied Yogic Anatomy

Yoga is a holistic discipline that takes into consideration not only the body-mind complex, but also the dimension of spirit. In order to truly comprehend the rationale of yogic health management principles and tap into the depths of its potentials, we need to understand the basic structure of the philosophy that is yoga.

Yoga speaks of two basic principles responsible for creation, be it on the macrocosmic level of the heavenly bodies, the 'normocosmic' level of our existence, or the microcosmic cellular and sub-cellular levels. They are the cognition principle and the action principle. All of creation comes into being due to the interplay of these two principles.

The cognition principle

As the name suggests, the cognition principle is responsible for perceiving, interpreting, analyzing, becoming and remaining aware of one's existence as an individual and of the individual in relation to the rest of creation. This is also known as consciousness or the 'intelligence principle'. The cognition principle is responsible for us being aware of what we are and what our surroundings are. The level to which our consciousness has evolved is responsible for the nature of our individual self. This principle, although present in all creation, both animate and inanimate, is evolved to differing degrees within each component of nature – such as rocks, soil, water, flora and fauna. The cognition principle is latent in rocks and minerals, is sleeping or minimally active in plants, is in a pre-waking state or sub-optimally active in animals and awake in humans. Human beings have crossed an important barrier in the evolution of consciousness, and this differentiates us from animals.

A stone exists, but it cannot express itself in any manner, nor does it know that it exists; plants exist, can barely express themselves and have no inkling of their individuality and existence; insects and animals exist and can express themselves better than plants, but they do not know that they know about their existence. Only in humans has cognition evolved sufficiently, not only to be able to know, but to be able to know that they know. Although, this cognition principle is able to comprehend and be aware, it is not able to act upon its knowledge or awareness. For this reason it needs the help of the action principle.

The action principle
The action principle is responsible for carrying out all the various activities that define life. It is responsible for creation per se, whether microscopic atoms, simple amoeba, plants, animals, humans or huge galaxies. All come under the jurisdiction of the action principle. The entire human body, emotions and mind exist due to the specific evolution of this action principle, which divides, re-divides and modifies itself into the various systems in the body, the sense organs needed to perceive and the motor organs needed to carry out the decided actions. This action principle, however, is unable to comprehend, cognate, analyze or decide upon the course of events to be acted upon. For this, it depends upon the cognition principle.

The merger
The cognition principle can see, but cannot act and the action principle can act, but cannot see. Hence, each of these, in isolation, is helpless to carry out productive activity.

Only when there is union of both can there be a coherent and powerful entity, not unlike the mergers seen in today's corporate world. The microchip from company A needs the computer motherboard from company B to carry out its processing. The company B motherboard needs the company A microchip to provide direction to its innumerable circuits. And only when both of these come together, do you have a complete computer able to carry out an amazing range of activities.

The cognition principle is also known as *Shiva* or *Purusha* and the action principle is also known as *Shakti* or *Prakriti*. With the merger of Shiva with Shakti, the Shakti principle differentiates and forms five different dimensions of human existence: the physical dimension or *annamaya kosha*, the bioplasmic energy dimension or *pranamaya kosha*, the mental-emotional dimension or *manomaya kosha*, the dimension of psyche or intuition, *vijnanamaya kosha*, and the dimension of blissful joy known as *anandamaya kosha*.

The physical dimension is the manifest dimension, while the rest are progressively subtler and function at deeper levels in the human being. All of us are aware of the physical dimension, many of us are aware of the mental dimension, while a few are aware of the energy dimension and almost none of us are aware of the psychic, intuitive and blissful dimensions of our personality. These dimensions are mutually related and interdependent. They figuratively cover the Shiva principle in concentric layers, and hence are also known as sheaths.

Annamaya kosha

Annamaya kosha, the 'food sheath', is the manifest, or physical dimension of human existence. The origin of this system depends on the physical food that we eat. The food we eat, containing proteins, carbohydrates, fats, minerals and all other nutrients, is broken down during digestion. It is absorbed into the body and the various components are used to make cells, supporting tissues, enzymes, hormones and other items according to the body's needs. The liver is important in this process. All these systems and organs: the five sensory organs, the five motor organs, the brain and other systems, form annamaya kosha, the physical, manifest dimension of human existence. Annamaya is the gross dimension, while the other four dimensions are progressively less gross or more subtle. Annamaya kosha is the base or substratum onto which the effects of the other four dimensions finally manifest. Any changes, modifications or shortcomings in the other four dimensions find their way to annamaya kosha and find expression or manifestation here. Accordingly, all diseases, regardless of their origin, finally manifest in the dimension of the body.

Pranamaya kosha
Prana refers to the vital energy present in all living beings. It is responsible for providing the energy needed for the activities of all the koshas. It is like electricity which is responsible for the working of the light bulbs, heater, fan, washing machine, microwave and computer. Without electricity, all the appliances we have come to rely on would come to a standstill. Similarly, prana is responsible for all the activities of the human being, including at the levels of mind and consciousness. Without prana, the entire being will come to a grinding halt and disintegrate rapidly.

Prana manifests itself in various ways. It exists in the cosmos as the undifferentiated cosmic prana, which is the primary source of energy for all forms of existence, whether living or non-living. This cosmic prana differentiates into the individual body and is then known as individual prana. Depending upon the degree of evolution of consciousness in the individual, the state of activation of prana also varies. Pranic energy is also known as the subtle life force, or in the Chinese tradition, the 'chi' which pervades the whole body.

The energy released from cellular chemical reactions, which supplies the energy for our bodily needs, is but a small, gross manifestation of this subtler and wider energy pattern.

60

The energy we use is just a small sub-unit of the pranic energy which yoga says lies latent within each individual.

Prana is the basis of our body's ability to exist. All other systems depend on pranic energy for sustenance. Pranic energy is also known as bioplasmic energy or the subtle force. Prana exists in nature as cosmic prana or *mahaprana*. It manifests itself in our individual bodies as kundalini, the supraconscious energy. Depending upon the level of evolution (evolution of consciousness, not just the body) of the individual, only a fraction of this energy is released in the body. This fraction manifests as the various pranas which carry out all the routine activities of the body. This cosmic prana is said to have descended into the body via specific energy centres known as *chakras*. These chakras are in fact important nodal junctions and trigger points for all the five koshas as well as for the level of consciousness of the individual.

While the cosmic prana pervading the entire cosmos is called mahaprana, the prana pervading the human body is known simply as prana. When the mahaprana enters the individual body, it is then known as prana. Based upon the function carried out, this prana is further divided into five main sub-pranas and five other smaller pranas. There are five main pranas.

Prana is located between the throat and the diaphragm. It controls the functioning of the respiratory system, including the oropharynx, nasopharynx, larynx, cardiac system and circulatory system.

Apana is located in the pelvic region between the navel and the perineum. It controls the functions of the genito-urinary system and gut motility, especially of the large intestines, excretory and reproductive organs.

Samana is located between the diaphragm and the navel. It activates and controls the functioning of the digestive and metabolic system and acts as a balancing or coordinating force between the two opposite forces of prana and apana.

Udana is located in the arms, legs and head. It is responsible for the sensory organs and the motor organs, and controls the sympathetic and parasympathetic nervous systems.

Vyana pervades the whole body. It regulates and coordinates the musculo-skeletal system, acts as a reserve or back up and also as a coordinator for the other four pranas.

Fig. 8.1: The Pranic Body

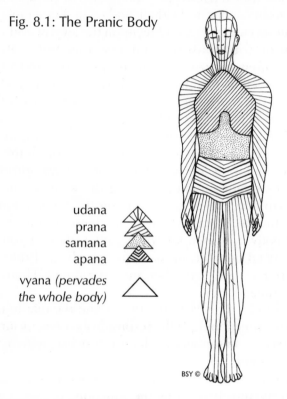

udana
prana
samana
apana

vyana *(pervades the whole body)*

BSY ©

Source of prana in the body

The cosmic prana concentrates in the body, lying dormant at the base of the spine, in the coccyx, as kundalini energy. A miniscule fraction of this energy is released in the body to carry out the multitude of activities, including the physical, mental, emotional, intellectual, psychic and other activities, which go on continuously in a living being. Through various yogic practices, it is possible to activate this dormant energy, which can then be utilized to carry out many other functions that remain inactive due to lack of sufficient energy. Additionally, a qualitative and quantitative increase in the quantum of prana directly affects the level of consciousness, as both are interlinked and interrelated with one another. Our consciousness starts expanding and many of the higher functions hitherto beyond the individual's capacity come within voluntary control. In lay terminology, this is also seen as the acquiring of supernatural powers. A full discussion on this topic is given by Swami Satyananda in *Kundalini Tantra,* published by Yoga Publications Trust. Suffice to say that activation of this latent energy is a powerful tool in the management of cancer.

A note of caution: Yogic practices dealing with kundalini awakening are to be undertaken only under the direct guidance of a kundalini expert or a guru. Without such guidance this activation can prove extremely detrimental.

Nadis

The pathways through which the prana flows in the body are known as *nadis*. The scriptures mention a total of 72,000 nadis forming a network throughout the body, each carrying out a specific function. These nadis correspond to the meridians used in the Chinese systems of acupressure and acupuncture. Within this network, there are three main nadis extending from the base of the spine in the coccyx to the hypothalamic region in the brain: ida nadi on the left, pingala nadi on the right and sushumna nadi in the centre. There are then another fifteen less important nadis, plus many more carrying the pranas to individual organs and tissues. It has been observed that when energy moves through these nadis, there are specific effects in the body such as the release of hormones, and changes in the mental thinking pattern and emotional states. Activation of certain nadis results in specific actions in the body and mind.

Disturbances in these nadis may lead to blockages, causing pranic depletion in certain areas. This results in cellular dysfunction of varying degrees. Cancerous transformation of cells is said to be due to chronic depletion of pranas combined with chronic distortion of the normal pranic flow pattern. In fact, any disease is said to be due to an improper pranic supply to that region or system. The scriptures mention that a proper pranic supply is essential for positive health and that perfection of certain yogic practices which manipulate the pranic generation and supply in the body can impart vitality, perennial youth, freedom from disease and even immortality. Of course, this depends on the ability to master the technique and to be able to invoke, generate and manipulate the pranas and the associated systems in the body.

For a more detailed exposition, *Swara Yoga* and *Prana Pranayama Prana Vidya*, published by Yoga Publications Trust, are recommended reading.

Manomaya kosha

The third dimension or manomaya kosha deals with (i) the gathering of perceptions received via the physical body through the sense organs, (ii) the cognition, analysis and assimilation of these perceptions, (iii) the imparting of further instructions based on these perceptions, and (iv) storage of these perceptions, their analysis, the action taken and the result obtained from that for future reference via the memory.

The organs used for this purpose are known as the inner organs or *antah karana* (as opposed to the *bahya karana* or outer organs, i.e. the five sensory organs and five motor organs). The antah karana is comprised of manas, buddhi, chitta and ahamkara.

Manas is the part of the mind that receives sensory impulses from the five sensory organs and prepares the raw information for further action. It acts as the first or temporary buffer area for incoming information.

Buddhi: The raw information from manas is transferred to buddhi. Buddhi analyzes the information, integrates it and 'makes sense' out of the huge mass of information arriving

64

from the five senses. It then categorizes and prioritizes it before proposing a plan of action based on the intellectual processes developed in the individual.

Chitta: The process of information arriving, being sorted, the nature of the action taken and its outcome is stored in chitta for future reference. When a similar event occurs again, buddhi draws on the previous experience as a precedent, analyzes the result of the action and then bases its present decision on this memory.

Ahamkara is that part of the mental matrix which colours and tries to alter buddhi's decision according to the whims and eccentricities of the individual. This depends on the individual's sense of correctness and appropriateness as well as the need to fulfil the basic desires and instincts inherent in a person. This is the ego-principle which influences the decisions made by buddhi through intellectual processes which are reinforced by the past experiencing of a similar event.

The next two koshas, vijnanamaya and anandamaya, relate more to collective consciousness than to the individual. It could be said that they are the bridge between the individual and the collective whole, also known as the supreme consciousness.

Vijnanamaya kosha

This dimension deals with the deep unconscious strata of our being. It enables those rare intuitive flashes of understanding which allow us to comprehend an event or situation from a totally different perspective. It is responsible for 'paradigm shifts' in our understanding. Discovery of the malarial parasite by Sir Ronald Ross is a perfect example of this dimension. Convinced that the mosquito carried the malarial parasite, but unable to isolate it, he observed batch after batch of slides under the microscope without success. One hot afternoon, utterly exhausted, he took a nap while still at work and dreamt of the exact structure and location of the malarial parasite. He awoke, took slides from a particular part of the mosquito and this time he was able to isolate the malarial parasite.

Similarly, the structure of the benzene molecule eluded chemists. In spite of all their efforts, no known method of atomic bonding could explain all the properties of the molecule. Kekule, an eminent chemist, had been trying to isolate the bonding pattern of benzene to no avail. One night he dreamt of six snakes encircling each other each, each holding the tail of the other in its mouth, forming a hexagon, and three other snakes adding to this strange structure at alternate nodes. The scientist awoke trembling and knew instinctively that he had seen the molecular structure of benzene.

Deep within us there exists a much higher store of knowledge. We can occasionally tap into this storehouse, the insight coming as a flash of intuition, a gut feeling, a vision or even in dreams. These intuitive flashes of knowledge cannot be explained, but when put to the test, provide the exact solution to previously insoluble problems.

Anandamaya kosha

This dimension is even subtler than vijnanamaya kosha. Its essence is *anandaswaroopa*, the innate joyfulness pervading our being. It manifests more easily in infants and younger children in whom manomaya kosha is not yet developed and hence does not overshadow anandamaya kosha. Very occasionally we feel good and incredibly happy for no reason. Nothing seems to go wrong at that time. These are the moments when we get a mere glimpse of this dimension of our being.

Interrelationship of the koshas

Each of these dimensions, in close coordination with the other four, plays a vital part in our existence and maintenance. The effects of the other four dimensions trickle down to the physical dimension or annamaya kosha. Annamaya kosha serves as the backbone of existence, the manifest dimension.

It is the dimension in which the result of the activities in all the other dimensions is finally seen. It serves as the major source of nourishment, as an interface between the individual and the rest of the world through the various sense organs, and through its motor organs is responsible for implementation. Manomaya kosha depends upon annamaya kosha for receiving sensory inputs and carrying out motor commands. Pranamaya kosha is the substratum of the whole system as it supplies prana, the vital energy needed for the existence and proper functioning of the other four dimensions. Vijnanamaya and anandamaya koshas provide guidance and direction to the individual. They are dependent on annamaya kosha to provide nutrition, information and also to carry out the impulses sent forth from the higher dimensions.

Why cancer develops: the yogic view

Disease is nothing but an imbalance or disturbance in any of the five dimensions of a human being. It can originate in any of these dimensions. This imbalance causes reduced functioning, non-functioning or malfunctioning in that particular dimension. If this disturbance is not contained and reversed, then it percolates down to the next less subtle dimension and manifests there as a malfunctioning of that dimension also. If it cannot be contained at that level, then it spreads further, progressively invading each kosha in turn.

Thus a malfunction in the physical body can either have its origins in the same dimension (due to injury, infection, environmental disturbance, etc.) or be a percolation from the higher dimensions, from anandamaya kosha to vijnanamaya kosha to manomaya kosha to pranamaya kosha and then finally to annamaya kosha. Conversely, a disturbance in annamaya kosha causes a corresponding disturbance in pranamaya and manomaya koshas too. The body-mind-spirit triad manages and succeeds in restoring balance within physiological limits. Chronic or powerful acute disturbances, however, disrupt this balance and cause a dysfunction, resulting in disease.

In chapters 4 and 6 we saw that cancer results from multiple, non-lethal and progressive genetic damage, causing activation of carcinogens along with loss of cancer suppressor genes. The neuropeptide stimulation sequence causing this damage can be due to external physical causes or internal causes arising from disturbances in the pranamaya and manomaya koshas.

These five dimensions are interconnected and changes in one dimension create fallouts in the next dimension and vice versa. Thus a negative change in anandamaya or vijnanamaya kosha would affect the next kosha, manomaya, which in turn would create ripples in pranamaya kosha, which correspondingly would affect annamaya kosha.

Risk factors for cancer

1. **Annamaya level** – physical factors (for a more complete list, see Table 1 in chapter 3)
   - contact with carcinogens such as tobacco, or exposure to certain substances (e.g. asbestos)
   - chronic injury or repeated physical irritation, such as a sharp tooth which causes repeated injury to the lining of the mouth, giving rise to a chronic ulcer, which then undergoes malignant transformation
   - Possibly dietary factors
   - Exposure to radiation.

2. **Manomaya level**
   - Mental activities causing recurrent negative emotions or thoughts
   - Powerful, emotionally-charged traumas
   - Inappropriate ego-defence mechanisms
   - Inappropriately high stress over an extended period of time.

3. **Pranamaya level**
   - Pranic blockages amongst the main pranic flow channels or nadis
   - Dietary imbalances or malnutrition causing pranic deficiencies

- Lifestyle patterns and events causing a blockage or deficiency in the chakras.
4. **Vijnanamaya and anandamaya levels**
Disturbances in these levels have greater collective ripples in the system. The commonest causes are:
- Blockages in the expression of messages coming from these higher causal levels
- Longterm lifestyles which are out of sync with the basic rhythms of our existence
- Deep-rooted suppressions, thoughts, phobias, neuroses
- Events and activities which create deep-seated emotional trauma, shattering of faith and psychic imbalances
- Activities which induce altered states and experiences interfere with the expression of these causal levels and can also create imbalances in them. Over a period of time this could lead to illnesses, including cancers of various kinds.

9

Yogic Cancer Management: Criteria and Parameters

With an expansion of our understanding of the human being from the physical level to higher levels comes the realization that the causative factors of cancer are not limited to the body, but go beyond this dimension. The logical step from here is that our definition of cure needs to widen its horizons to include these levels also. For even if the disease process has not yet manifested in the physical body but is present in the mental or pranic or causal body, it is just a matter of time before it is experienced in the physical body. Hence, we will now look at how to restore normality to the physical, mental, pranic and causal dimensions.

Cancer is caused by the presence of some unbalancing forces, be they physical carcinogens, dietary factors, lifestyle factors, repressed thoughts with a strong emotional content or chronic mental and emotional stress. When the mind plays and replays thoughts over and over again, it results in stimulation of the same patterns of neuropeptides which, over a period of time and due to their cumulative effect, lead to pranic blockages and pranic depletion in corresponding areas. It is postulated that this aggravates immune suppression and a generalized debility of the entire psychoneuroimmune apparatus. In this state the body is denied the protective shield which mops up the errant cancerous transformations under normal circumstances. The continued presence of these factors allows mutational damage of the genetic structure

70

(stimulation of oncogenes and suppression of cancer suppressor genes) to flourish.

Thoughts, emotional content and stressors can originate externally or internally. Internally, they can arise: a) from the conscious mind due to brooding over certain recent or past instances, desires and ambitions, b) from the subconscious or even the unconscious mind from the distant past, and c) even from the collective unconscious, including from past lives. These processes collectively prepare the substratum or the field for cancer to strike.

It then takes only a small trigger in the form of carcinogens from the diet or other physical carcinogens to cause the advent of cancer. The lesion may then be maintained and fostered by the thought processes and other factors mentioned above, causing the cancer to become aggressive in its spread, resistant to treatment and, of vital significance, creating the basis for relapses of the cancer.

Summarizing, carcinogens can either be physical or mental in nature. They create a strong impression in the cellular memory and over a period of time may result in mutational changes in the DNA of the cells which, if the circumstances are unfavourable, can escape the DNA repair mechanisms and immune surveillance and become a part of the genetic material of the affected cells. These mutations are then carried forward in progressive cell divisions and may either progress or be rectified. If these oncogenic mutations survive and progress, they can lead to cancer. Under such circumstances progression to cancer may occur.

Yogic cancer management
Yogic cancer management aims to:
- Block the action of one or more of these carcinogenic activities at various levels, thereby preventing a build up of the cancerous transformative processes so that they remain below the critical threshold level. This prevents the translation of cancer predisposing conditions into cancerous conditions.

- Bring about harmony amongst all the various dimensions so that there is a smooth flow of energy and the stress faced by the individual becomes 'eustress' (positive stress) rather than 'distress.' This prevents the immune system from being overloaded with signals towards which the immune system has to direct its energies. Thus, the immune apparatus has a better chance of attending to cellular disturbances in the form of microtumours and destroying them before they can cause permanent damage.
- Boost the performance of all the systems, most notably the circulatory and psychoneuroimmune systems, though a variety of mechanisms. This improves their functioning and increases the chance of the system preventing the occurrence of the disease. If the disease is already present, these systems are better able to manage the disease.
- Introduce positive healing factors which not only neutralize the disrupting effect of the carcinogens (physical, mental, emotional and causal), but actively boost the psycho-neuroimmune apparatus, thereby causing reversal of the cancerous process.

In annamaya kosha (the physical level), there needs to be an optimization and balance in the various organs and systems, like the digestive, respiratory, cardiovascular, haematopoietic, neuro-endocrinal, genito-urinary and others. This can be achieved by a set of asanas, shatkarmas and yogic dietary habits.

In pranamaya kosha (the pranic level), pranic blockages need to be removed, the deficiency in prana needs to be attended to and a smooth, unhampered flow of prana all over the body needs to be attained. This can be achieved by various practices of pranayama and the practices of prana vidya and prana nidra.

In manomaya kosha (the mental-emotional level), the thought patterns need to be managed, the emotions need to be channelled and given a constructive outlet, and a harmonious blending of these two aspects needs to be attained. This can be achieved by relaxation and the premeditative practices of pratyahara and dharana, and by integrating the principles of the yamas and niyamas in our day-to-day lives.

In vijnanamaya and anandamaya koshas (the sub-conscious, unconscious and collective unconscious), we need to tune in to the various impulses that originate there, propelling our thought processes, ambitions and drives, and manage them appropriately using various meditative practices.

Yogic approach
Yoga cancer management suggests a four-pronged approach:
1. **Yogic practices** which directly affect the erring neuro-peptide patterns, normalize and bolster the flagging prana and set right the dysfunctional mental-emotional patterns. This includes asana, pranayama, various relaxation and meditative practices and mantra chanting. Regular daily practice sessions are needed to bring about normalization.
2. **Yogic lifestyle**, meaning changes in the life patterns, causing distinct changes within the body. Yogic lifestyle means having a way of life which is in harmony with the natural body rhythms, while still meeting the demands presented by the modern world. Living in this way plays a major role in the reduction of stress. It includes integration of yogic principles as well as the values of the yamas and niyamas in daily life.
3. **Yogic diet**: Food, being one of our most primal needs, is very closely linked with strong emotions. As such, the diet plays an important role in yoga cancer management. A yogic diet involves:
   - *What we eat*: the rule of thumb is to eat plenty of fresh vegetables, fruits and foods that provide appropriate nutrition. This means the inclusion of sufficient macronutrients (carbohydrates, fats, proteins and water) and micronutrients (vitamins, minerals, antioxidants and phytochemicals). Reduce meat products and avoid excessive processed foods, barbecued and oily foods.

73

- *When and where we eat*: food should be consumed in a suitable atmosphere and frame of mind as the emotions aroused during the ingestion of food become linked with the food itself, affecting the quality of the food and its subsequent effect on the body.
- *Why we eat*: the maxim 'eat to live; not live to eat' has never been more important. Living to eat implies that we are transferring some of our unexpressed emotions on to food, creating an association which may have adverse effects at a later time.

4. **Yogic atmosphere**: Our surroundings have a profound impact on the quality of life. The presence of both environmental and thought pollution is detrimental to the ecosystem and also to ourselves.
   - Inclusion of specific practices such as tree care and tree worship help to re-establish our connection with nature and her rhythms.
   - Fire ceremonies, or yajnas and havans, are another set of particularly powerful practices which can alter the atmosphere dramatically.
   - Chanting of mantras or having a recording playing in the background releases positive vibrations which have a subtle effect on our psyche. Some useful mantras are given in Appendix 2.
   - Yantras (geometrical figures) have a strong impact on the psyche. Placing appropriate yantras on the walls of the house contributes to the process of change that is being set in motion by the yoga practices. See chapter 31 for further discussion of yantras. Some common yantras are given in Appendix 1.

In this way, we can 'starve' the cancerous process of its source by eliminating the carcinogenic factors, whether in the physical, mental-emotional or causal dimensions. Secondly, we reinforce the positive patterns in our system, thereby nourishing the protective and regulatory systems of the body (the immune, endocrine and nervous systems). This boosts their performance and increases their chance of reversing any damage that has already happened. Thirdly, we tap into the higher dimensions. The pranas are activated and blockages in the pranic pathways are cleared, thereby establishing a free flow of energy and the removal of toxins. Tuning into the higher dimensions of vijnanamaya and anandamaya koshas provides us with healing, positive energies which sustain and nourish healthy life patterns. With this approach, we can attempt to reverse the cancer process and re-establish positive health.

10

Useful Yogic Practices:
An Overview

In order to achieve the changes needed to tackle cancer and the entire gamut of problems which forms its retinue, yoga has in its kit bag a wide variety of tools which can be practised in combination to achieve the above-mentioned results. Swami Satyananda, a leading authority on yoga, emphasizes the importance of maintaining practicality while practising yoga. He calls this the yoga of common sense. For example, it would be foolhardy to expect a patient with advanced symptoms of cancer to perform very difficult asanas. It would be more appropriate to include pranayama and yoga nidra and other relaxation and visualization practices that are within the capacity of the patient.

It is important at this juncture to be very clear about the aim of the yogic practices being undertaken. The aim is neither physical flexibility and postural expertise, nor attaining altered states of consciousness. It can be summarized as raising the pranic levels in the body, thereby enabling the body's natural defence systems to overcome the cancer in the body and also to neutralize the ravaging effect it has on the body. With this in mind let us understand the mechanism of action of the main yogic practices.

The main yogic practices useful in yogic cancer management are:
1. Asanas
2. Pranayama and prana vidya

3. Shatkarmas
4. Bandhas and mudras
5. Yoga nidra and prana nidra
6. Yamas and niyamas
7. Antar mouna, ajapa japa
8. Nada yoga
9. Meditation practices – guided imagery or visualization practices
10. Yogic diet
11. Yogic or ashram lifestyle
12. Amaroli
13. Other higher practices such as tattwa shuddhi and certain kriyas.

Each of these practices is complete in itself. However, a proper integration helps us speed up the process. Each practice aims at a certain part of our personality as the starting point for the transformation, and its effect gradually spreads to all other parts of our personality. Be it hatha yoga, raja yoga, kundalini yoga, nada yoga or any other type of yoga, the effect is the same, transforming the entire personality.

Asanas, bandhas, mudras and shatkarmas begin with the physical body and proceed from the body to the mind, emotions and psyche, removing imbalances which create limitations in functioning.

Pranayama and prana vidya aim at the pranic substratum of our being. Correcting the limitations in this dimension, these practices very quickly and effectively transform all other dimensions (annamaya, manomaya, vijnanamaya and anandamaya koshas) as prana is the support, the energy upon which all other dimensions depend.

Antar mouna, ajapa japa and other meditative practices touch the deep unconscious base of our beings, which is the storehouse of all the *samskaras*, or past impressions and memories. They drop cleansing seeds into the deeper layers of our consciousness. These seeds begin the changes there which are reflected in the other dimensions or koshas. When

77

practised under proper supervision, these practices can be extremely powerful, capable of creating miraculous changes.

Other practices such as nada yoga, karma yoga, diet and amaroli affect multiple dimensions simultaneously and bring changes in all the dimensions almost simultaneously.

If a single practice is capable of bringing about such dramatic changes within ourselves, an appropriate integration of all these techniques into a few short practices should be able to more than compensate for the lack of time that one faces when cancer is snapping furiously at one's heels. Time is of great importance in illnesses like cancer when one does not have the time to practise and master every practice in order to derive the desired outcome. In such cases, an integration of all these practices acts like small fires heating a pot of water simultaneously from multiple sides. The effect is synergistic and the water heats up much faster than if only one fire was burning. This is an important principle in managing cancer through yoga.

The practical aspects of practising and integrating these different types of yoga will be discussed in more detail in following chapters. Please note that the practices should be undertaken only under the guidance of a trained yoga teacher/therapist.

11

Asana, Pranayama and Prana Vidya

ASANA

Asanas are simple physical postures which are performed and maintained comfortably for varying durations of time. They affect the musculoskeletal system, the internal organs and particularly the neuro-endocrine system. Modern lifestyles impose a heavy sensory load on the human nervous system, resulting in its chronic over-stimulation. This leads to fatigue, loss of mental acuity, and emotional fragility.

Asanas act by:

1. Modulating the body's response to stress and stimulation and helping the system to tone down unnecessary activation of the response systems. As well as the sensory nerves and motor nerves there is yet another set of nerves which carry the kinaesthetic impulses from the body to the brain. These kinaesthetic impulses are the feedback messengers to the brain. Asanas modulate feedback to the brain, reducing brain activity to an optimal level.
2. Massaging the internal organs, thereby improving the blood flow and removing accumulated toxins.
3. Reharmonizing the hormonal levels in the body.
4. Favourably altering the metabolism patterns in the body.
5. Stimulating specific energy pathways and activating the corresponding chakras.

Important points to be aware of in asana practice are:

- The posture of the body as it moves from the starting position to the final position.
- The breathing pattern and synchronization of the breath with the asana movement.
- Reaching and maintaining the final posture without undue strain or effort.
- Awareness of the body and especially certain trigger points, usually the appropriate chakra or the chakra kshetram, which deepens the effect of the asana. These are unique to each asana.
- The number of repetitions of the posture.
- Balancing both sides of the body by giving equal time to the left and right sides in asanas where applicable.
- At the end of each physical round, the effect of the asana can be accentuated by visualizing it being performed mentally while simultaneously taking the awareness to the parts of the body that are involved.
- The sequencing of asanas, so that where relevant a pose is followed by a counter pose.
- Asanas may be practised at any time of day except after meals. The best time is the two hours before and including sunrise. The two hours around sunset is also a favourable time.
- Avoid strain during asana practice. Never exert undue force while doing asanas. Practise only according to individual capacity and energy level. Always consult a trained yoga teacher before commencing asanas.

For detailed instructions, consult *Asana Pranayama Mudra Bandha*, published by Yoga Publications Trust.

PRANAYAMA

Pranayama is derived from the Sanskrit root words 'prana' and 'ayama'. *Prana* refers to the pranic energy or subtle force pervading both the cosmos and the human system. *Ayama* means extension or expansion. So *pranayama* actually means

80

extension or expansion of pranic energy in the whole body so that all activities are carried out optimally. The subtle pranic energies are activated and regulated by manipulating the breathing pattern, thus also taking into consideration the needs of oxygen for the body.

The process of respiration provides us with oxygen which is separated from air and selectively absorbed into the blood in which it is transported all over the body tissues, right down to the cellular and sub-cellular levels. There are two types of respiration: external and internal. The process of inhaling air from the atmosphere to the lungs is external respiration, and the process of oxygen and carbon dioxide transportation from the lungs to the cells and vice versa is known as internal respiration. The entire process is very delicately managed via constant feedback and communication between the body tissues and respiratory and other centres in the brain.

There is a wealth of data showing that changes in the rate and depth of breathing produce changes in the quantity and kind of chemicals (e.g. neurotransmitters and hormones) that are released from the brain and also from other parts of the human system. These chemicals relay information between different parts of the brain and between brain and body, and dramatically affect the activity of the brain (including thoughts and feelings) as well as other physical organs. It is important to note that these chemicals affect the breath, and the breath affects the chemicals.

Mode of action of pranayama
1. Specific centres in the brain fire off impulses which control the movement of the respiratory muscles, thereby controlling respiratory activity. These centres are intimately linked by neuronal circuits to the hypothalamus and other centres in the brain. While the basic activity of respiration is involuntary in nature, the higher centres of respiration are under voluntary control. As such, respiration is a partially voluntary activity. It is also affected

strongly by the autonomic nervous system (which includes the sympathetic and parasympathetic systems).

The rate and depth of respiration changes according to the needs of the body. Not only are the rate and depth of respiration affected by the brain and the autonomic nervous system, but the brain and autonomic nervous system are also affected by the rate and depth of respiration. Pranayama makes use of this intimate connection for our benefit. Hence, if we consciously alter the rate and depth of respiration, it induces corresponding changes in the mode of functioning of the brain and body. This includes physiological changes in the blood vessels and in the functioning of organs, including the heart. It also includes changes in the feelings and thoughts.

2. Pranayama also releases endorphins. These are nervous system chemicals which induce a sense of joy and wellbeing as well as boosting the various functions of the neuro-immune apparatus. It is postulated that they may have a role to play in blocking the activation of oncogenes in promoting healthy activity of cancer suppressor genes.

3. It is common in daily life to have a breathing pattern that is quite shallow and irregular. Conscious deep breathing or yogic breathing changes the way we breathe. It uses the lungs to optimal capacity while helping to calm the mind. This helps maintain optimal functioning of all systems.

4. Pranayama practices induce changes on the pranic level, helping to clear pranic blockages in the *nadis* (the network of pranic channels) throughout the body.

5. Pranayama normalizes the pranic level in the body and alleviates any pranic depletion which has taken place.

6. Pranayama affects the functioning of the nose, which in turns affects the sense of smell and has a direct link with mooladhara chakra, which is responsible for deep unconscious drives, including sexual drives and emotional responses. Mooladhara chakra is also the abode of kundalini, the storehouse of potential energy. Regular pranayama practice stimulates kundalini, releasing more

82

energy into the system and also clearing blockages and releasing deeply suppressed emotional and unconscious blocks by appropriate purification of the chakras in general and mooladhara chakra in particular.

7. Normally while breathing, only one of the nostrils is active while the other nostril is inactive. After about 90 minutes the dominance of the nostrils changes. This is a natural phenomenon carried out via the impulses of the autonomic nervous system. According to swara yoga, the rhythm of nostril activity and its cyclical alternation is disturbed by mental patterns, inappropriate lifestyles, imbalances between physical and mental activities and stressful occurrences, to name just a few factors. The alternate nostril breathing technique employed in nadi shodhana pranayama helps to balance the nostril activity, which in turn balances the sympathetic and parasympathetic flows in the body.

Amongst the many pranayama practices available, the main ones useful in cancer management are yogic breathing, nadi shodhana, bhramari, ujjayi and cooling pranayamas like sheetali and sheetkari. Heating practices like bhastrika or kapalbhati are *not* recommended.

Nadi shodhana pranayama (alternate nostril breathing)

Nadi refers to the pranic channels which form a network throughout the body, and *shodhana* means purification. Therefore, *nadi shodhana* means purification of the pranic channels so that prana can flow unimpeded around the body. This is one of the most important pranayama practices as without purification and cleansing of the channels, prana will not be able to reach the organs. In cancer there is a cumulative blocking of the pranic channels, resulting in pranic depletion in a specific area. As already noted, this leads to cellular degeneration and mutations. Regular practice of nadi shodhana pranayama clears up these blockages, replenishes prana not only in the specific region, but also throughout the body, activates the latent psychic and pranic pathways and stimulates the generation of prana in the body.

83

Nadi shodhana is practised by alternating the inhalation and exhalation between the left and right nostrils. This is the most important characteristic of the practice. Building on that basis, there are four components which are used in various ways, depending on the experience of the practitioner. These are:
1. Inhalation or *pooraka*
2. Exhalation or *rechaka*
3. Internal breath retention or *antar kumbhaka*
4. External breath retention or *bahir kumbhaka*

The appropriate ratios of duration of each component and the details of the pranayama should be learnt from a trained yoga teacher and be practised regularly over a long period of time. The basic form for beginners involves inhalation and exhalation only. This should be done for five rounds at a time, and limited to a maximum of two sessions a day. Progression to the next levels should only be done under the guidance of a trained yoga teacher.

Bhramari pranayama (humming bee breath)

Bhramara means bee. In this pranayama, we imitate the bee by making a humming sound. Regular practice of this pranayama has multiple advantages. It reduces anger and stress levels, improves blood circulation in the brain, removes toxins from the cerebro-spinal fluid, boosts the immune system and hastens healing. It also harmonizes the mind and attunes the body systems with the mind.

Ujjayi pranayama (the psychic breath)

This important practice is the foundation that must be established as a preparation for the higher practices of prana vidya. The aim is to become aware of the breath while making a soft whispering or hissing sound during inhalation and exhalation. A useful tip is to contract the throat as if you are about to swallow water or saliva. The slight contraction created in the lower throat just before swallowing needs to be held while breathing. This immediately induces a state of tranquillity and serenity and has a strong impact on the psychic state of the individual. Integrated with awareness and visualization of the breath, this leads to an almost effortless balancing of the mental, pranic and other causal dimensions. This results in activation of the pranas and enhances the function of the nervous and immune systems. Hence its profound effect on the healing and repairing capacity of the body.

Sheetali (cooling) and Sheetkari (hissing) pranayamas

These are tranquillizing pranayamas which reduce excessive heat in the body and bring about a cooling effect.

Important points for pranayama practice

- *Breathing*: Unless otherwise specified, always breathe through the nose without undue effort or strain.
- *Time*: The most conducive time for pranayama is *brahma-muhurta* or the time between 4 am and 6 am. Just after dusk is also a suitable time for pranayama practice. Always try to maintain the same time for pranayama or for any yogic practice.
- *Location*: A quiet, clean, well-ventilated room is best. Avoid practising under a fan or in air-conditioning. Fresh, unpolluted air is of prime importance. Practising in places that are naturally high in prana compounds the effect: for example, beside a lake, waterfall or the ocean, in a valley, forest or on a mountain top. Avoid practising in direct sunlight or in a windy place.
- *Asana or posture*: Siddha/siddha yoni asana or padmasana are the best postures for pranayama practice. If you are unable to maintain these postures comfortably, adopt any posture in which you can relax while keeping your spine, head and neck in a straight line. Sit on a blanket or a thickish rug made of natural materials.
- *Sequence*: Pranayama is practised after asanas and before meditation when used in conjunction with these practices.

- *Clothes*: Wear loose, comfortable clothes. Care must be taken to ensure that abdominal movement is free and unrestricted by a belt, trouser buckle or anything tight.
- *Food*: Pranayama should never be practised on a full stomach. There should be a minimum gap of three hours between the last meal and the practice of pranayama.
- *Avoid strain*: With all pranayama practices, it is important to remember not to strain and not to try to increase your capacity too fast.

For detailed instructions, consult *Asana Pranayama Mudra Bandha* and *Prana and Pranayama*, published by Yoga Publications Trust.

PRANA VIDYA

Prana vidya is a very powerful psychic tool, which awakens the prana and trains us to manipulate the pranas consciously. Although traditionally the final aim of prana vidya practices is expansion of consciousness, which leads to meditation and perfect union, awakening of the pranas is an important by-product which induces powerful healing activity in the body. It is this by-product that we are interested in for the management of cancer.

Prana vidya consists of a number of stages in which the awareness and control of the prana in the body are progressively developed. The first step is to become aware of the presence of prana in the body. The next stage is to be able to purify and voluntarily move the pranas in the body. The next stage of the practices is to awaken the dormant pranic forces within ourselves. All these use a combination of pranayamas, mudras, bandhas and visualization sequences. Prana vidya is an extremely powerful tool in combating cancer, as the yogic viewpoint on the causation of cancer holds that pranic depletion and distortion is a basic cause of cancer.

Traditionally, the practices of prana vidya are considered to be advanced practices and were imparted only to a select few who would not misuse them. However, prana vidya practices are extremely beneficial in revitalizing the pranic levels in the body, hence they are included in the management of cancer. It is essential to observe all the rules of prana vidya to derive the correct benefit and to avoid any detrimental side effects. The practices should be learnt under the guidance of an expert yoga teacher/therapist. For details of these practices, refer to *Prana, Pranayama, Prana Vidya*, published by Yoga Publications Trust.

12

Shatkarmas or Detoxification

Shatkarmas are a set of cleansing or detoxifying practices. Practising them regularly leads to the elimination of physical as well as mental toxins. We have seen that diseases are caused by imbalances created in the body-mind-spirit system. The aim of shatkarmas is to eliminate these imbalances and restore the equilibrium. These practices also have corresponding parallels in Ayurveda.

According to Ayurvedic principles, diseases are caused by imbalances among the three *doshas* or humours of the body: *vata* (wind, gas), *pitta* (bile) and *kapha* (mucus, phlegm). There are two schools of treatment for diseases in Ayurveda. The first is a milder form known as *shamana* practices, in which imbalances are brought back to normal by means of various herbs. This process is known as 'pacifying the doshas'. In this system, the excess or disturbance is not removed but neutralized. As such, there is always a possibility that this fragile balance might again be disrupted by the causative factor. The second school of treatment is known as *shodhana* or purification practices, also known as *pancha karma* practices. With these, the erring doshas are eliminated from the body and purified so that the imbalance is removed from the system. These practices are highly sophisticated. Special training is needed for their practice and there are specific indications and contra-indications.

The six purificatory practices, or *shatkarmas* of the hatha yoga system, are the psychic parallels of the above *pancha karma* practices. They act by restoring pranic balance between the two main pranic pathways of ida and the pingala, thereby achieving physical, mental and even spiritual purification. The set of six detoxifying practices are: neti, dhauti, nauli, basti, kapalbhati and trataka.

1. NETI (NASAL CLEANSING)

Neti is a cleansing and purifying process for the naso-pharyngeal tract. The two main practices included in this category are: *jala neti* (using warm saline water) and *sutra neti* (using a specially prepared cotton thread). To better understand the mechanism of action, we need to first understand the nose.

The nose

The nasal passage is a very sensitive pathway. The lining of the nasal passage is characterized by the presence of a rich nerve supply, which makes it very sensitive to changes in the nervous system, particularly the autonomic nervous system. It is also an important part of the immune system and has a rich blood supply. Changes in the cardiovascular, nervous and immune systems can therefore cause changes in the lining of the nose. Nasal bleeding being more common in pregnant women, and 'blocked nose' when the immune system is fighting off a virus, are good examples of the nose's sensitivity to the activities of other body systems. As all communications in the body are essentially bi-directional, this implies that changes in the nasal tract are accompanied by corresponding changes in the entire network of the neuro-endocrine and immune pathways.

The nose is also the seat of the olfactory or smell sensation. Smell is one of the most primitive senses, and has a very strong impact and association with memories and events. When unresolved over a long period of time, these can lead to the formation of 'mental carcinogens', which cause cancerous transformation of cells, depending upon the particular predisposition of the individual. Clearing of the nasal passages and their gentle stimulation with warm saline water or a thread or catheter by means of neti causes a normalization of these pent-up memories by triggering them through stimulation of the smell receptors. Once triggered, the memory is played out mentally as emotions, visions or remembrances and the energy locked up in that particular memory is released. Of course, this is a gradual process and one must remember not to have unrealistic expectations from these practices.

According to swara yoga, the nose is also a powerful trigger for various pranic pathways in the body-mind system due to the fact that it is richly supplied with nerves and nadis. It is also intimately linked with ajna and mooladhara chakras. Ajna chakra is the centre controlling pranic activity, the development of wisdom, forgiveness, synthesis of intuition and also the centre for awakening psychic abilities. Mooladhara deals with emotions relating to security, possessions and reproduction that can manifest as greed, lust, power, hunger and other related behaviours. It is also the place where many psychological complexes originate and become locked, causing many dysfunctions. Proper stimulation of these chakras causes release of these repressions and blockages.

Cancer management using neti
With this background, it is easy to realize neti's mechanism of action, which can be summarized as follows:
1. Physical cleansing of the nasal passages, leading to better breathing and fewer toxins reaching the lungs.
2. Stimulation of the autonomic pathways balances the sympathetic and parasympathetic flows throughout the body. This results in a reduction of unnecessary stimulation to the entire body, especially the neuroimmunoendocrine apparatus, and boosts its functioning.

90

3. Cleaning, clearing and activating the pranic pathways of ida and pingala responsible for conducting prana throughout the whole body-mind. This promotes healing, reverses degeneration and reduces malfunctioning.
4. Psychic cleansing of mooladhara and ajna chakras results in the removal of many 'mental carcinogens.'

2. DHAUTI AND BASTI

The next category of detoxifying practices is *dhauti,* cleansing of the gastro-intestinal tract. Five common practices in this group are:
1. *Varisara dhauti*: In Sanskrit *vari* means water. In this practice the entire gastro-intestinal tract is cleansed using water. It is also commonly known as *shankhaprakshalana.*
2. *Vahnisara dhauti*: *Vahni* means fire. This refers to the effect of the practice, i.e. stoking up the digestive fire, and increasing peristalsis to clear the accumulated debris in the digestive system. This practice is commonly known as *agnisara kriya* and *nauli kriya.*
3. *Vamana dhauti*: *Vamana* means forced regurgitation. This practice uses induced regurgitation as a means for clearing the upper gastro-intestinal tract. In *kunjal kriya* the induced regurgitation is assisted by drinking a large amount of warm saline water.
4. *Vatasara dhauti*: *Vata* means air. This practice uses atmospheric air as a cleansing agent for the gastro-intestinal system.
5. *Vastra dhauti*: *Vastra* means cloth. This practice uses a specially prepared length of lint-free cloth as a cleansing agent.

Basti is a method of cleaning the intestines using medicated liquids to stimulate the colon and rectal canal and cleanse them thoroughly.

91

The digestive tract

The digestive system comprises the mouth, pharynx, oesophagus, the small intestine (duodenum, jejunum, ileum) and the large intestine (caecum, ascending colon, transverse colon, descending colon, rectum and anal canal). In addition to this basic structural grouping, the functional grouping also includes the liver, gall bladder and the pancreas. At this stage it is useful to summarize some important and relevant points regarding the digestive system, especially those that have a bearing on the formation and management of cancer.

Management of cancer using dhauti and basti

The digestive tract has a huge network of neurones along the entire length of the tract. The number of neurones found here rivals the number in the brain itself. In addition to this, the lining of the tract is filled with receptors for neuropeptides, many of which act as neurotransmitters in the brain. Interestingly, in addition to releasing various enzymes in response to the food present in the digestive system, these neuropeptides are also responsible for stimulation or inhibition of the immune apparatus and for transmitting impulses in the brain for carrying out various activities. Their heavy presence in the digestive tract points to the huge amount of feedback sent by the digestive system, and the potential source of origin of errant signals causing the mutations responsible for cancer.

Hunger and the relationship with food are some of the most primitive drives in all animals and humans. As a result, they play a major role in the formation of psychosomatic disorders. The same connection holds true with bowel habits, anal activity and the human personality. The practices of dhauti, such as kunjal, agnisara kriya, shankhaprakshalana, nauli and vastra dhauti all strongly stimulate these primitive reflexes, releasing blocked and pent-up emotions, thoughts and karmas. This can lift a huge load from the psycho-neuroimmune apparatus. This means that along with the cleansing of the stomach and gastrointestinal tract on the physical level, there is also a massive overhauling on the pranic and mental-emotional plane.

These practices clean the digestive tract, recalibrate the enzymal flow (and with it the corresponding neuropeptidal flow) patterns in the whole body. They also improve the functioning of the liver, which is the metabolic epicentre of the body. There is a profound effect on manipura, swadhisthana and mooladhara chakras from the churning up of dormant samskaras which lie in these energy centres. Mooladhara is the storehouse of kundalini, which is the fountain source of prana, while manipura is the generator station of prana. Churning up and cleaning these two major pranic centres improves pranic levels in the body, thereby improving the body's ability to overcome cancer.

Precaution: As these practices are extremely potent and have strong side-effects if wrongly performed, it is essential that they are learned and practised under the guidance of a competent yoga teacher/therapist. They will not be appropriate for every individual with cancer, nor at every stage of the disease process.

3. AGNISARA KRIYA AND NAULI KRIYA

The mechanism of action of these two practices is quite similar. Both massage the abdominal organs and tone the digestive system, strongly stimulating the digestive activities and functions. They also stimulate manipura chakra, the pranic storehouse in the body, and have a marked effect on the five pranas, rapidly raising their levels in the body.

4. KAPALBHATI AND TRATAKA

Unlike the other practices, which focus mainly on the five sense organs, their neuro-hormonal connections and the chakras associated with them, these two practices concentrate mainly on the sixth 'sense organ' – the mind. Yogic scriptures speak of the mind more descriptively, calling it the *antah*

93

karana, or inner sense organ. The antah karana receives and processes information, forms associations, integrates relevant data from the sense organs, storing it for future reference, and forms opinions from all this information (the functions of manas, buddhi, chitta and ahamkara respectively). The mind is given higher guidance by ajna chakra and these two practices create patterns that activate this chakra.

Kapalbhati (frontal brain cleansing)

Kapalbhati is a specific pranayama which incorporates quiet, passive inhalation followed by forced, rapid and active exhalation. By reversing the usual active inhalation and passive exhalation pattern, kapalbhati cleanses the 'mental carcinogens', figuratively wiping the slate clean. It purifies ida and pingala nadis, energizes the mind, removes mental distractions and tones the nervous, respiratory and digestive systems. Appropriate additions of other practices, such as bandhas (psychic locks) and visualizations, add to the effectiveness of this practice.

Precaution: It is, however, essential to remember that kapalbhati should be avoided after the onset of cancer, especially before and after chemotherapy or radiotherapy, as it a heating pranayama and can have negative repercussions.

Trataka (concentrated gazing)

Trataka is a simple visualization and concentration practice using a symbol such as a black dot or a candle flame. Regular practice of trataka either using a candle flame or a symbol is a very powerful practice for unlocking the capacities of ajna chakra. Ajna is the final distributor of prana, the overall control and coordination centre, and the pathway for opening up the higher vijnanamaya and anandamaya koshas. Awakening of these koshas results in tapping into higher forms of healing energies. Trataka also helps by balancing the nervous system, harmonizing the sympathetic and parasympathetic flows and reducing nervous tension, anxieties and worries, thereby bringing a definite change in the neuropeptide secretion patterns in the brain and in the body. The effects are seen as improved vitality in all cells in the body, improved immune function and greater capacity of the body for repair and regeneration.

Cancer management using kapalbhati and trataka

Kapalbhati (when not contra-indicated) and trataka are very powerful tools in cancer management. They launch a multi-pronged attack on cancer in the following ways:

- By bringing old, unhealed feelings, emotions, thoughts and psychological patterns to the surface and ensuring their controlled and harmless channelling.
- By stimulating ida and pingala nadis, which leads to improved pranic circulation in the system.
- By improving the repair and regeneration response mechanisms in the body.
- By activating ajna and vishuddhi chakras, which are responsible for tapping into the higher realms of our being, vijnanamaya and anandamaya koshas.
- By developing our ability and awareness to respond proactively to situations, thereby avoiding the build-up of future 'mental carcinogens'.

Important practice note

Shatkarmas bring about purification in the body-mind: (i) by expelling physical and mental toxins, and (ii) by recalibrating the entire body physiology so that blockages are cleared and excesses are brought back to normal. These practices have specific indications, contra-indications, precautions and restrictions, and should be practised only under the guidance of an experienced yoga teacher/therapist. The sequencing of these practices and the following of dietary restrictions need to be rigorously adhered to. As might be expected, these practices must be followed by certain relaxation techniques to help the body recover from the rigours it has been subjected to. Yoga nidra followed by simple visualizations is highly recommended.

13

Bandha and Mudra

We have seen that dissipation, distortion, depletion or blockages in the pranic flow in the body are mainly responsible for diseases, including cancers. Various yogic practices such as asanas and pranayamas help in correcting these imbalances, while shatkarmas overhaul the system and expel both the mental and physical toxins.

Bandhas, or psychic locks, and *mudras,* or psychic manipulations, provide an excellent, efficient and yet simple means of concentrating, directing and maximizing the effect of the liberated pranas in the body. In addition to just preventing dissipation of the pranas, these practices also help to channel the pranas, especially when they are invoked and activated using the various prana vidya practices.

BANDHAS

Bandhas are psycho-muscular energy locks. A bandha is applied by a combination of breath retention and physical contraction of specific muscles. Proficiency leads to complete voluntary control over the semi-voluntary sphincters governing the urinary, genital, and anal movements and the ability to reverse the direction of contractions. Classical texts mention the ability to draw into the bladder increasingly viscous fluids such as water, honey and finally even mercury via the urinary tract. This ability to reverse the direction of contractions in these muscles leads to reversal of the flow of sexual energy. A concentration of this energy generates a subtle substance called 'ojas', which is said to have almost miraculous properties. In addition, bandhas also provide control over respiratory, digestive and metabolic activities.

Bandhas have a specific action on the physical level, through the muscles and their corresponding neural connections. Their main action is, however, via stimulation of the pranic channels and chakras, and their ability to redirect the pranic flow in the body through ida and pingala nadis. Another effect is on the pranas. Apana, which normally flows downwards from the navel, is reversed and made to flow upwards by uddiyana bandha. Prana, which normally flows upwards within the chest, is reversed by jalandhara bandha, so that it flows downwards, meeting apana. This meeting releases a massive amount of energy and kindles the yogic fire (yoga agni). The yogic fire is then able to burn away toxins and induce rejuvenation. The main bandhas are:

1. **Moola bandha** (perineal contraction or lock): This lock is applied by selective contraction of the perineal muscles, so that the central portion of the perineum is lifted upwards while keeping the rest of the region relaxed. The trigger point in males is the perineal body, a fibrous bead located at the centre of the perineum. The corresponding trigger point in females is in the area of the cervix. The main action is on mooladhara and swadhisthana chakras. This bandha helps to redirect sexual energy, awaken the pranas and clear various emotional blocks.

2. **Uddiyana bandha** (abdominal contraction or lock): Application of this psychic lock causes a negative suction force in the abdominal region, causing a massive redistribution of blood, nervous impulses and pranic energy in this region. The downward flowing apana is reversed, flows upwards, and joins prana. This collision causes a production of heat and energy which jump starts manipura chakra, the generator of pranic energy in the body. Hence, stimulation of manipura chakra causes a rise in the pranic level and its

97

general redistribution all over the body-mind. Since prana is the basis of the functioning of the entire body-mind apparatus, a rise in pranic levels causes spontaneous realignment of bodily functions, especially the ability to fight disease (a function directly related to manipura chakra). This lock is applied during external breath retention.

3. **Jalandhara bandha** (throat lock): At the end of exhalation, the chin is brought down to the base of the throat, locking the breath and food passages. The flow of blood, lymph and prana in the chest cavity is deeply influenced by this lock. It activates of anahata and vishuddhi chakras. Locking the throat at the end of exhalation causes a negative pressure in the chest cavity (the mediastinal cavity). This changes the biomechanics of the blood and lymph flow in this region. It also creates a change in the normal pranic flow patterns, thereby stimulating vishuddhi chakra. Activation of vishuddhi chakra initiates various purificatory processes in the body-mind. These changes affect the immune system, the endocrinal system and also the metabolic system, which has a cascading effect on the entire body-mind.

4. **Maha bandha** (the great lock): Maha bandha combines all three bandhas in one practice.

MUDRAS

In Sanskrit, the term *mudra* means a gesture or a form. In yoga mudra is a specific posture which stimulates the chakras, activates the pranic pathways and finally aids in awakening the latent kundalini energy.

Pranic energy is continuously flowing throughout the body. When it is manipulated to create a concentration at certain trigger points, and this is coupled with certain asanas, pranayamas and breath retention, the result is activation of dormant pranic pathways. In addition, these practices also awaken the higher koshas, vijnanamaya and anandamaya koshas. This is the basis of the action of mudras.

Of the various mudras available to us, the following are the most useful in cancer management: shambhavi mudra, nasikagra drishti, khechari mudra and shanmukhi mudra, prana mudra, vipareeta karani mudra, vajroli/sahajoli mudras and ashwini mudra. Practice details of these mudras can be found in *Asana Pranayama Mudra Bandha* and *Yoga and Kriya*, published by Yoga Publications Trust.

14

Yoga Nidra and Prana Nidra

YOGA NIDRA

Yoga nidra is an exquisitely simple yet effective tool for relaxation and rejuvenation. The practitioner lies down in shavasana and listens to the instructions given by the teacher. Although yoga nidra appears to be a relaxation technique, it is much more than just that. It is an entire system of deconditioning the mind, releasing unnecessary, irrelevant events and associations stored in the subconscious and unconscious mind, and training the mind in appropriate responses. To use a computer analogy, it is the equivalent of clearing the cache memory and unwanted cookies, emptying the recycle bin and temporary files, defragmenting the hard drive and running the disk doctor and speed disk or disk optimizer . . . all in one go!

Yoga nidra includes the following components:
1. Preparation and relaxation
2. Resolve
3. Rotation of consciousness around the body
4. Breath awareness
5. Awareness of sensations and feelings
6. Visualizations and chakra awareness
7. Resolve
8. Externalization.

Resolve

Willpower, or *iccha shakti*, is a major force which, successfully harnessed, can help us overcome any barrier. It is said 'Faith can move mountains'. To successfully harness this great potential, the thought processes, whether conscious or unconscious, need to be focused in the same direction. Intellectual reasoning can only take us a short distance. It cannot exert any influence on unconscious thoughts and emotions. Over-reliance on the intellect becomes a barrier in this process of reorientation.

According to Swami Satyananda, a *sankalpa* or a resolve made at the beginning and at the end of yoga nidra is like a seed sown in the deeper layers of consciousness. He tells us that anything in life can fail, but not the sankalpa or resolution made at the beginning and end of yoga nidra. The transformation taking place through the sankalpa is not imposed from without, but is a blossoming from within.

According to psychologists, our thoughts, actions and behaviours are driven by impulses originating from the conscious, subconscious and unconscious mind. The sankalpa reaches deep within these layers and acts from there in a twofold manner: by initiating strong, focused, result-oriented impulses for the psyche to act upon, and by acting as a lighthouse for other dissipated and mutually conflicting impulses. The sankalpa orients these directionless impulses, aligning them with the sankalpa. This can be compared to the light emanating from an ordinary bulb which spreads out in all directions and is unable to reach long distances, as opposed to the same amount of light being processed into a laser beam, so that all the rays have the same frequency and direction. The laser beam is so powerful that not only can it traverse hundreds of kilometres, but it can even penetrate and cut through solid steel. The sankalpa in yoga nidra acts as the processor which converts an ordinary light beam into a laser beam.

Body rotation

The next component in yoga nidra is body awareness. It is derived from the tantric system of nyasa, an essential procedure in almost all tantric rituals. It is considered to be the foundation on which other sadhanas are based. The parts of the body are identified and specific mantras are used to invoke appropriate energies into them. Swami Satyananda, with his deep insight into tantric lore combined with sharp scientific acumen, has modified this system so that we can benefit from it without knowing the Sanskrit names or mantras. As the awareness is rotated systematically around the body, nerve impulses are transmitted between the brain and the specific part. This leads to increased awareness and according to yoga an increase in the blood flow to these parts. This increase enhances oxygen delivery to and waste removal from the tissues. Simultaneously, the pranic channels in that region are activated, pranic blockages are cleared and pranic levels in these areas are replenished. Visualization of the body parts and mental repetition of their names triggers and releases any associated unconscious processes pre-occupying the mind.

Breath awareness

The awareness is then shifted to the breath, which is subtler than the body. Specific respiratory centres in the midbrain coordinate the usual, involuntary breathing process. When awareness is brought to breathing, higher parts of the brain, such as the cerebral cortex (involved in thinking and planning) are activated. Breath manipulation thus changes the activities of the brain.

Self-regulated awareness of the breath implies a sense of control and has a very strong harmonizing effect on the whole nervous system as well as affecting pranamaya kosha.

Awareness of sensations and feelings

The awareness is now taken to a subtler level still, that of the emotions, feelings and sensations. This also involves visualizations and chakra awareness. This process acts upon manomaya, vijnanamaya and anandamaya koshas, releasing many unexpressed or repressed emotions and deeply buried samskaras. In addition to the cleansing of these koshas, this dharana (concentration) practice unlocks the potential of the deep unconscious and taps into the vast, unlimited healing powers of vijnanamaya and anandamaya koshas.

Yoga nidra and cancer

Apart from the devastation that a cancerous process wreaks in the body, it also inflicts an enormous pressure on the mind, emotions and psyche. People with cancer can feel the pressure of facing death and coming to terms with it almost too strong to bear. This pressure saps the willpower of the person, who may sink into terrible gloom, experiencing deep insecurities and negative thoughts. These, of course, only contribute to the feeling of being in a deep abyss with no return. The patient can mentally give up hope, resigning themselves to the prospect of death. In the body, this translates as the inability of the protective mechanisms of the body to fight back, meaning that all is lost. It is extremely difficult to face the onslaught of all the fears, insecurities and negativities that surface in the face of cancer.

Yoga nidra helps by enabling relaxation even when in the grip of such extreme stress. It also provides a harmless channel for the expression of these fears, as they can be played out on the mental screen while in this relaxed state, losing much of their edge and becoming manageable. By providing an outlet for these negative emotions, yoga nidra neutralizes the deeply debilitating impact of the negative mental state on the psycho-neuroimmune apparatus. When mastered, the visualization component of yoga nidra is extremely useful in enhancing the healing and regenerative capacities of the body-mind.

Mechanism of action of yoga nidra in cancer management

1. Sankalpa improves willpower and provides direction to the scattered and shattered mind.

103

2. Rotation of awareness reduces the high state of baseline stimulation back to normal states, induces deep-seated relaxation, improves blood circulation and replenishes the depleted pranic levels in the body.
3. Removes hindrances and unnecessary overloading of the psychoneuroimmune apparatus, thereby improving its performance.
4. Redirects pranic energy by setting up pranic currents through visualizations and other instructions.
5. Pranic energy is redirected towards building up defence mechanisms and repair and regeneration activities.
6. Chakra awareness activates the pranic circuits and increases the total quantum of available prana in the body.

PRANA NIDRA

Prana nidra is the logical extension of yoga nidra. In this practice, pranic energy is invoked and distributed to specific parts of the body along the pranic pathways. According to yogic theory, disease is a result of improper pranic dynamics in that specific region. The primary causes might be many and varied, but distortion in pranic dynamics is the root of any disease. Prana nidra combines certain powerful prana vidya practices with the practice of yoga nidra. After rotation of body awareness is completed, instructions regarding visualizations are given to invoke the pranas. The prana then rises up the ascending pathway and is distributed systematically all over the body via the corresponding chakras. The affected area is then subjected to specific rounds of 'pranic wash' after which the pranas are systematically released back along the descending pathways to the base of the spine.

The basic components in prana nidra are:
1. Resolve (as in yoga nidra)
2. Body awareness (as in yoga nidra)
3. Chakra awareness (as in yoga nidra)
4. Awareness of ida/pingala pathways looping across the chakras

5. Movement of prana along the sushumna pathway
6. Pranic bath: A bath is considered to be a purifying practice. A cold shower freshens up the mind, while a long luxurious warm bath removes tiredness and tensions from the body and has a very relaxing effect. Similarly, a pranic bath washes all the internal organs with a flood of pranas directed towards each organ respectively and removes the pranic deficiency or distortion building up at that point. The process involves visualization of the pranas arising from mooladhara to manipura to ajna along the sushumna pathway. They are then distributed among the chakras and along the pranic pathways to the important organs like the brain, the lungs, the abdomen, liver, intestines, kidneys, etc. Visualization and coordination of pranic movement with the breath and visualizing the clearing of blockages along the pathways can be coordinated with the breathing process also. A greater emphasis can be laid on diseased organs and their associated parts; e.g. the lungs in lung cancer, the abdomen and stomach in gastric cancer, and so on.
7. Returning the pranas to mooladhara via ajna and the sushumna pathway
8. Body awareness
9. Resolve.

The practice of prana nidra is a very powerful tool, which when mastered, is extremely useful in all types of cancers. In addition to its use in yogic health management, it can also easily be used prior to and just after chemotherapy and radiotherapy in order to accentuate the targeting of the therapeutic agent as well as to reduce its side effects.

15

Yama and Niyama

The *yamas* and *niyamas* are guidelines for social and personal codes of conduct respectively, as presented in the system of raja yoga. Although the social plane is an important sphere of practice for the yamas and niyamas, positive social behaviour is not the primary reason for their importance in raja yoga. Rather, they are there to assist our quest to tap the total potential of the mind. To do this, it is necessary to free the mind from the numerous background processes which dominate so many of our mental resources. All the practices that have been discussed so far help to increase the capacity of the mind by helping with concentration, clearing and purification.

By regulating our outlook, thoughts and behaviour, the practices of yama and niyama aim to reduce the clutter in the mind by preventing it from even arising. These practices streamline the thoughts, behaviour and speech of a person so that negative energy feedback loops are minimized. This is a classical case of nipping the problem in the bud. There are five yamas and five niyamas.

YAMAS

1. *Ahimsa* – absence of violence
2. *Satya* – truthfulness
3. *Asteya* – honesty

4. *Brahmacharya* – sensual and sensorial continence and abstinence
5. *Aparigraha* – non-attachment towards and non-accumulation of possessions.

NIYAMAS

1. *Shaucha* – cleanliness on both the physical and mental planes
2. *Santosha* – contentment
3. *Tapas* – austerity
4. *Swadhyaya* – self-study, introspection
5. *Ishwara pranidhana* – surrender to Ishwara, the regulating principle behind the cosmos.

The mind is like the memory bank of a surveillance camera. The mind (conscious, subconscious and unconscious) receives inputs from all the five sense organs (smell, touch, hearing, vision and taste), the five motor organs and also from the organ of inner perception, the *antah karana*. The antah karana is composed of four sections: *manas* (receptor of impressions), *buddhi* (intellect, the rationalizer), *chitta* (the storer of information) and *ahamkara* (the self-identifier or ego). All this information is stored in the mind in the form of associations. The yamas and niyamas serve to minimize the feedback loops and thought processes created by conflicting thoughts, behaviour or speech.

They act like firewalls used to protect computers from infiltration by viruses, trojans and spyware. They prevent the entry of dangerous negative thought currents, which undermine the health status of the body-mind, and also create habits which correct any negative thoughts which may have already seeped in. Integrating the yamas and niyamas in our day-to-day life can be a taxing exercise if one does not exercise common sense and practicality while doing so. They should be introduced gradually, so that there are no unwanted psychological 'side-effects'.

Role of the yamas and niyamas in cancer management

Cancer can be caused by the repression of feelings and emotions over an extended period of time. Guilt complexes, phobias and other neuroses compound the problem. Intelligent use of the yamas and niyamas helps to reduce the formation of these unhelpful feelings and hang-ups. The practices of swadhyaya, shaucha, tapas and ishwara pranidhana are especially useful in dealing with mental patterns that already exist and which may be causing much mental turmoil and anguish.

A diagnosis of cancer usually leads to deep brooding as to the cause, and often the mind starts jumping to wild conclusions. Each and every past mistake (either true or perceived) comes into the mind and is gone over again and again. Although this is a natural response, it is extremely hazardous as it hampers progress towards recovery. Practising the yamas and niyamas is a perfect way of channelling energy, which may otherwise be spent on meaningless brooding, into a more fruitful, result-oriented self-improvement exercise. The yamas and niyamas help us to implement the saying, 'failures are stepping stones to success,' by providing a means to learn from our mistakes and create a better today and tomorrow.

16

Antar Mouna, Ajapa Japa, Nada Yoga, Visualization

So far we have seen a number of ways and means of understanding and manipulating the various subtle body processes which yoga recognizes. We have dealt briefly with the first steps of yoga – asana, pranayama, mudra, bandha, shatkarma, yama and niyama. These practices deal with the external aspect of human functioning and interaction and hence are known as *bahiranga* or exoteric yogic practices. After becoming familiar with and competent in these practices, it is time to delve deeper into the body-mind. For this we need to move from the external aspect to the internal aspect of our personalities.

The next step is pratyahara, which helps us move from the external aspect with which we are so familiar to the internal aspect about which everything seems to be Greek and Latin. *Pratyahara* deals with withdrawing the senses from external objects and redirecting them within. The meaning of pratyahara is explained by the example of the turtle. A turtle can voluntarily withdraw its four limbs, tail and head within the hard shell it carries on its back. In the same manner, through the practices of pratyahara, we learn how to withdraw the mind from the five senses and turn it within.

In Patanjali's raja yoga system, pratyahara is the fifth limb of raja yoga. It also means withdrawal or retreat. To be able to master pratyahara practices in a scientific manner, we need to develop a proper understanding of the mind, the thoughts and their influence on our personality. Unless we are able to withdraw our senses in a systematic manner without any suppression, it will not be possible for us to utilize this energy in a constructive manner, be it for meditative purposes or therapeutic purposes. It is important to note here that withdrawal of the senses does not mean going into a hazy dream state. Instead, it is a state of heightened awareness of the internal processes occurring within the mind. The input signals come not from the outer sense organs but from the *antah karana*, the inwardly-oriented sense organs.

ANTAR MOUNA

One of the most important and comprehensive practices of pratyahara is antar mouna, or inner silence. *Antar* means inner and *mouna* means silence. This is a practice that brings about inner silence. External silence is achieved when there is no input from the five senses. Inner silence comes about when our thoughts, emotions and other mental gymnastics are silenced. This technique is relatively easy to practise, yet has profound implications at the therapeutic as well as the spiritual level.

We have already seen that pranic energy, the vital force or subtle force, underpins all the activities of the body and mind. All activities in the five koshas depend solely upon pranic energy. If the pranic energy is distributed over too vast a network, it is logical that the quantum of prana reaching each unit of the body will be less. Those systems which receive sub-optimal pranic energy over extended periods will eventually malfunction. Hence, the necessity and importance of withdrawing from outside stimuli and concentrating the pranic energy within, so that it can be made available for the process of healing and regeneration.

Antar mouna helps us achieve this. Antar mouna has six stages. It commences with simple awareness of sense perceptions, moves on to awareness of spontaneous thought processes, then the posing and disposing of thoughts, and

110

other stages in which the thoughts are managed in specific ways. As we work through the stages, we progressively become aware of the thoughts, their origin, their progression, their intended or expected result, and so develop the ability to consciously and voluntarily control these thoughts. It is essential here to be aware of the difference between this scientific, graded analysis and blind and brutal suppression of thoughts. The practice of antar mouna ultimately leads to the state of thoughtlessness in which the mind becomes still and is receptive to our mental instructions and suggestions.

AJAPA JAPA

This leads us to ajapa japa, where we become aware of the spontaneous natural breath and the subtle sounds accompanying it. *Japa,* or mantra repetition, becomes *ajapa* or spontaneous when the mantra automatically repeats itself without conscious effort. Ajapa japa originates from the heart whereas japa originates from the mouth. Ajapa japa can take an aspirant from the most elementary level of body consciousness and environmental awareness to the highest stages of meditation. Its practice eventually brings all the desires, fears and complexes of the mind to the mental surface. When this occurs, the practitioner should view these mental scars and the vast mass of attached mental and emotional baggage with the attitude of a witness or indifferent observer. This facilitates the release of the mental groove created by the event, freeing the mind of its tensions, which are the root cause of most physical and mental illness.

Any mantra can be used during the practice of ajapa, although *Soham* is the mantra traditionally used as it corresponds with the natural sounds of inhalation and exhalation. Many practitioners have also achieved great results with the use of their guru mantra.

Every sound has a specific vibration which resonates with specific parts of the body. When that frequency is attained, it resonates with that particular part of the body, activating

111

that part. Ajapa japa combines awareness with imagination and visualization to intensify its effect. One has to become aware of the natural sounds accompanying inhalation and exhalation. During inhalation a soft, high-pitched sound of '*Sooooooo*' is experienced at the nostrils and throat, while during exhalation there is a lower frequency sound of '*hammm*'. When our awareness extends to this natural phenomenon and experiencing it in this way becomes second nature, we combine it with awareness of the frontal and spinal psychic passages.

Ajapa japa and cancer

Ajapa japa awakens the psychic passages and activates the chakras especially manipura, anahata and vishuddhi chakras, each of which has a major role to play in activating the pranas, transmuting emotions and feelings, and purifying the body.

Breath awareness, by reverse stimulation to various parts of the brain associated with the respiratory centres, reduces neuronal overload. This frees a huge amount of unnecessary stimulation of the psychoneuroimmune apparatus, which can then concentrate on managing the cancerous growth taking place in the body. This also helps us to better manage the emotions and their expressions, enabling us to channel our feelings into positive forms of expression.

NADA YOGA

Nada is subtle sound vibration. Nada yoga practices have a very important role to play in yogic cancer management, especially in being able to reconnect to life and thereby regain balance. This reconnection is an outcome of setting right many diverse networks in the body-mind ranging from abstract emotions, to calming the frazzled and overworked psychoneuroimmune system. To achieve this, we need a medium which can affect multiple areas all at once. Nada yoga fulfils this requirement to the hilt and can bring about a very subtle change in the body-mind, resulting in the release of many unspent and hence misdirected neurotransmitter circuits.

The potency and efficacy of sound vibrations is very widely documented down the ages in almost all civilizations and religions, as well as in modern physics and medical literature. The rampant use of ultrasounds, sonar devices and other remotely operated instruments bears testimony to this fact. Sound vibrations have been manipulated and put to use for a long period of time. Sound, when properly harnessed, travels through all mediums and can be a very effective means of change and transformation. It can easily be converted to other forms of energy also.

The practices of ajapa japa and nada yoga harness sound vibrations to exert an influence on the deeper aspects of the personality. Modern scientists and ancient religions both agree on the principle that sound waves have primordial existence and that matter evolved through them. Physicists speak of the Big Bang theory wherein everything existed in an extremely dense wave form at a single point (called singularity) from which the entire cosmos came forth. The Bible also speaks of a similar phenomenon, although in a more figurative manner. It says, "In the beginning was the word (sound) and the word was with God and the word was God." The Upanishads speak of *Aum*, the primordial sound, that has the entire cosmos and divinity inherent within itself. Yoga considers this 'original' sound to be *para* or transcendental sound.

An entire field of esoteric science was developed under the banner of tantra, which deals with sound vibrations and their effect on the chakras. The science of mantra also finds its origin here. Music and the classical fine arts are also based on the same principles. The action of mantras is seen to take place by the following mechanisms.

- Mantras are energy packets with the capacity to trigger deeper layers of the mind and bring about a complete transformation in the basic structure of the mind.

- They also stimulate the pranas and their pathways in the body.
- Mantras have specific effects on the chakras and can activate various dormant functions in human beings.

Four stages

Nada yoga classifies sound into four broad stages:

1. *Vaikhari* is audible sound originating from the acrobatics of the larynx or voice box when air rushes out from the lungs through the larynx. This sound is most comfortably used by beginners, whether practising kirtan, chanting, japa or music.
2. *Madhyama* is produced by moving the lips. Soft whispering without any audible sound is its hallmark. Once the mind is comfortably focused on vaikhari, or audible sound repetition, then one can gradually try to include madhyama sound in their practices.
3. *Pashyanti* is mental sound, the sound that reverberates in the mind long after the external original melody has been played and fallen silent. It is the sound that is made up of mental frequencies, and is more subtle than madhyama and vaikhari. Pashyanti arises spontaneously when the nada or music sung in vaikhari or madhyama is internalized.
4. *Para nada* is transcendental sound of extremely high frequency. The scriptures say it has gone beyond vibration and its nature is that of light. It is the unstruck sound perceived not by the physical ears but at anahata chakra, the heart chakra. This is the sound of revelations and divine songs.

   The main practices of nada yoga can be classified as:
- Mantra practice: chanting of mantras and other beneficial chants.
- Chakra anusandhana: the seven basic notes in music correspond to the seven major chakras.
- Vocal or instrumental music.
- Singing kirtan.

These practices are extremely useful as they touch upon all dimensions of the human personality and can be practised by almost anyone in some form or other, no matter their circumstances.

VISUALIZATION PRACTICES

Usually we have little or no control over the thoughts we think or the images that come to our mind. Once a certain pattern of thought comes, it is very difficult to get rid of it. This is of special relevance in relation to cancer as a deluge of negative thoughts with very strong emotional content follows the diagnosis, throwing us off balance completely. Unable to manage these thoughts, we can become overwhelmed by their sheer magnitude and power.

The thoughts and images that arise in the mind have a great influence on the neurohormonal peptides that travel along certain pathways in the body. These neuropeptides are responsible for transmitting information all around the body. They influence the activity of various organs and hence are known as 'informational substances'. Thoughts, emotions and mental imagery modulate their levels in the body, activate or inhibit their secretions and consequently have a deep impact on our internal physiology.

Guided imagery has a great role to play in the outcome of cancer therapy. Visualization practices improve our ability to formulate images, visions and thoughts at will and to manipulate them. This helps in managing the negative thoughts which surface during various stages of cancer therapy.

The mind has a tendency to be distracted and jumps from one thought to another like a monkey. When a thought or an image has a strong emotional or mental association, the mind tends to fall back time and again on the same thought or pattern of thoughts, resulting in brooding. With the practice of antar mouna one can train the mind to work on a single thought or a train of thoughts, images and so on and discard them at will. The thoughts are stored within our consciousness as images and associations. Hence, the capacity to create images at will helps us to manage the strong emotions that surface during cancer therapy.

It is best to begin with simple visualizations consisting of day-to-day objects. The yoga therapist instructs the practitioner to visualize certain objects on the mind-screen in front of the closed eyes. It is usual to start with simple, familiar images from nature and then introduce other material objects, phenomena, colours and shapes. Gradually, more complex scenes and series of events are introduced.

This guided imagery can then be used to directly influence the cancerous growth. For example, the tumour mass, its location and extent can be visualized, and then seen being steadily eaten away by the immune cells in the body. When the patient is receiving doses of chemotherapy or radiation, they should visualize the medicines or radiation waves homing in on the tumour mass and attacking only the tumour mass while sparing the rest of the tissues. These practices enhance the action of chemotherapy and radiotherapy. In this way the process of meditation through visualizations and associations can successfully be utilized as yet another useful tool against cancer.

Important note

The practices explained in this chapter should be learnt under the guidance of a qualified yoga teacher/therapist.

Refer to *Meditations from the Tantras* and *Yoga and Kriya*, published by Yoga Publications Trust, for practice details.

17

Some Higher Yogic Practices

Higher yogic practices usually combine visualizations, asanas, pranayama and other exoteric yogic practices. The important and relevant practices are kriyas and tattwa shuddhi. These practices are very powerful and are not recommended except without direct guidance, for they can bring out powerful stuff deep from the unconscious mind and such experiences can be very hard to handle and channel. Hence, these practices should be learnt under the guidance of a well trained teacher, and performed for small durations of time only, in combination with other appropriate extroverting techniques such as certain asanas, karma yoga or light, selfless physical activity. These combinations prevent an excessive rise in energy and also provide a constructive and simple channel for the amount of energy generated and stimulated.

KRIYA YOGA

Traditionally, kriya yoga practices can be performed only after one has a reasonable grasp of the earlier more exoteric and simpler practices of asanas, pranayama, bandhas and certain visualizations. The aim of these practices is to be able to awaken the dormant kundalini energy at mooladhara chakra. These practices are extremely powerful and can activate the chakras and pranic pathways very fast.

In yogic cancer management, we plan to use the by-product of these practices – awakening of the pranas and the chakras, for it is through them that the healing energies will flow and help to manage the disease process.

There are twenty main kriya practices which can be broadly classified into two groups: pratyahara practices and dharana practices. The pratyahara practices are a combination of certain asanas along with bandhas, chakra awareness and other practices to internalize the mind. The dharana group of practices focuses mainly on internal and not external practices.

Advanced yoga practitioners can combine these practices into their cancer management modules after due discussion with an expert teacher/therapist. However, the preliminary practices of *chakra shuddhi*, purification of the chakras, and the first six kriya practices can be practised by almost all under appropriate guidance. The advantage of these practices is that they help to stimulate the very channels which asanas and pranayama activate without having to perform much physical movement. This is especially beneficial in cases where a malignant growth prevents the active usage of asana and pranayama.

The six practices are:

1. *Vipareeta karani mudra*: Reversing the flow of nectar from the navel centre (manipura chakra) back to sahasrara chakra after being duly purified and transformed at vishuddhi chakra. If the inverted shoulder stand pose or vipareeta karani asana are unable to be performed, the practitioner can just lie down in shavasana, the relaxation pose, and complete the rotation of consciousness along the chakras. This also imparts similar benefits to the practitioner.

2. *Chakra anusandhana*: Awareness of the major chakras and kshetras (trigger points).

3. *Nada sanchalana*: Rotation of the mantra *Om* along the chakras.

4. *Pawan sanchalana*: Rotation of the breath along the chakras.

118

5. *Shabda sanchalana*: Rotation of the sound consciousness (*Soham*) along the chakra pathways.
6. *Maha mudra*: Rotation of breath awareness along the chakra pathway, incorporating other associated mudras such as khechari and shambhavi, and bandhas such as moola bandha.

When practised in moderation, these six kriyas have the capacity to jump start the flagging pranic levels in the body. They also help in purifying and clearing many blockages in the pranic channels, thus helping the pranas reach all over the body, especially in diseased regions.

TATTWA SHUDDHI

Our body evolves from the five elements or *pancha mahabhootas* (ether or space, air, fire, water and earth). These elements, in turn, evolve from the principles of Shiva and Shakti (see chapter 8). Impurities in these elements result in various imbalances and diseases. Cancer is no exception to this law. Indeed, the earth, fire and air elements are considered to be maximally deranged and impure in the cancerous process.

The practice of *tattwa shuddhi*, or purification of the elements, is in fact a prerequisite in almost all higher sadhanas; the concept being to purify the whole body, mind and psyche to make it ready for higher experiences.

Tattwa shuddhi can be practised in ten stages. The total practice need not take more than thirty minutes.

1. Kaya sthairyam
2. Chakra awareness
3. *Hamso* awareness
4. Yantra visualization and mental bija mantra repetition
5. Dissolution of the elements
6. Awareness of the papa purusha
7. Transformation of the papa purusha
8. Bhasma bath
9. Visualization of the Devi and experiencing her grace
10. Gradual externalization of awareness.

In yogic cancer management, the aim becomes to restore the balance and nature of the elements, so that the normal homeostatic functions of the body, mind and psyche can continue. This practice is a very useful tool to prime the mind for the modifications and manipulations that are needed to reverse the misdirected energies of a cancerous growth. It can be practised once a week as a routine, and also before and after radiation or chemotherapy to improve and channel their effects. When used in conjunction with other practices, it can prove to be a very effective self-healing tool. Tattwa shuddhi should be learnt under the guidance of a qualified yoga teacher/therapist.

18

Diet and Lifestyle

Diet and nutrition

Our entire body, the annamaya aspect of our being, is formed entirely by the food that we eat. The body comprises over three trillion cells, working continuously in close coordination and perfect alignment. Each of these cells is made up of many cell organelles. Structurally, all the cells are basically made of amino acids (from proteins), carbohydrates and fats. The body manufactures all these structures according to the blueprint provided by the DNA present in each cell.

The raw material for these finished goods comes from: (i) the reservoirs already present in the body and (ii) the food that we eat. If the raw material supplied is deficient, of poor quality or adulterated, then it goes without saying that the finished goods will be of poor quality and unable to perform to the desired levels. For this reason the diet has to be monitored and very closely modified according to the specific needs of the body-mind.

The second aspect is the mental diet. All the thoughts that come to our minds have a contributory role to play in the nourishment of the mind. The mental and emotional frame of mind that exists while eating is even more important in this respect. When physical food is being eaten to nourish the body, the accompanying thoughts, mental and emotional states nourish the mind. Hence it is important that the mental

121

framework and the thoughts are positive, constructive and happy while preparing and consuming food.

Our aim in diet modification is twofold:

1. *To build up the body's nutrition on the macro and micronutrient level*: This is essential as the cancer process drains a lot of energy from the body through its parasitic nature. The body also faces metabolic overload due to the rapid generation and destruction of cells. This means that the needs of the body in this state are quite different from its needs in a normal state.

2. *To address the subtler aspect of food* by generating positive, healing and wholesome thoughts associated with eating. In addition to enriching the calorific and wholesome value of food, the subtler force or the pranic content of food also needs to be enriched.

Diet – the physical aspect

The first aspect or the grosser aspect of nutrition is achieved by adopting a wholesome nutritious vegetarian diet which supplies the required amount of proteins, carbohydrates, fats, water, vitamins and minerals in appropriate quantities. Research has shown that many items in our diet act as behaviour response modifiers (BRMs). They have the capacity to modify the response of the bodily processes to various stimuli which can either be positive or negative. Many food items are thought to possibly increase the risk of some cancers, and are known as carcinogenic items. On the other hand, other foods may reduce the risk of cancer, known as anti-carcinogens. It goes without saying that our diet should contain as many anti-carcinogenic items as possible and avoid any carcinogenic foods. Details of these foods are described in chapters 3 and 5.

Diet – the subtler aspect

From a yogic perspective, food is not just inert matter which provides mere calories and nutrients. It is an important source of prana. Some food items have negative, vitiated and destructive pranic energy. Ingestion of these foods disrupts the normal pranic flow and balance in the body. The cumulative effect of such prolonged pranic deviations, sometimes spread over generations, predisposes or actually manifests as a cancerous tumour.

Yoga gives food an importance beyond basic nutrition. The *Taittiriya Upanishad* explains that the five elements evolved from the supreme consciousness. From the atman came ether, from ether came air, from air came fire, from fire evolved water and from water came earth, and from earth arose herbs, from which all other life forms arose. All structures, whether of the body or mind (which is a function of bodily activities) depend upon food. If the food we eat is tamasic, impure and low in energy, our body and mind will be of a tamasic quality. If it is rajasic, these qualities will be strong, and if the food is sattwic or pure, we will reflect sattwa. Therefore, we need to pay attention to the quality of the food we eat.

Tamasic food is unhealthy, stale, produces negative emotions and mental patterns, affects the pranas and induces physical disease. *Rajasic* or stimulating food induces desires and ambitions and, if not properly channelled or balanced, can also create health problems. *Sattwic* food, on the other hand, is fresh, light, rich in prana and most importantly helps to create positive patterns in the body and mind. In addition to the inherent nature of the foodstuff, the method of cooking also affects the quality of food. In dealing with cancer it is essential to eat a proper balance of sattwic and rajasic foods.

Yogic diet and fasting

To help prevent cancer, yoga prescribes a light sattwic diet which is nutritious, rich in prana and easy to digest and assimilate. Once cancer has struck, the diet needs to be modified so that it can become therapeutic and not just preventive. At this stage, yoga prescribes a diet with no animal products except organic unadulterated milk or buttermilk, adequate quantities of fresh fruits, vegetables, sprouts, salads and plenty of fresh water. (Please bear in

123

mind that these are *general* guidelines, which need to be modified according to individual need.) The foods should be freshly cooked, with minimal use of oils. Food can be cooked by steaming, boiling or roasting. Frying, barbecuing, stale food and chemically preserved or processed old food items should be avoided as they are tamasic in nature and detrimental to the pranic system.

Yogic principles also classify food by taste. There are six primary tastes: sweet, sour, salty, pungent, bitter and astringent. Yoga prescribes a diet with all six tastes present in proper proportions. A diet high in sweet and salty foods with prolonged neglect of the other tastes is said to be one factor leading to chronic diseases like cancer and diabetes. Our diet needs to be balanced with food of all flavours, so that it contains all the tastes with an emphasis on reducing the sweet taste. Sattwic food is good to taste. Rajasic foods are pungent, salty, or sour, cause burning or have a heating effect on the system. Tamasic food is tasteless, processed, fermented and unhealthy.

Yoga recommends a judicious combination of sattwic and rajasic foods. The proportion should tilt more towards sattwic food as its qualities can neutralize excessive rajasic and tamasic qualities already existing within us.

Another simple way to neutralize rajasic and tamasic tendencies is to observe a fast at periodic intervals of time. This helps to reduce tamas and bring out the sattwic nature within us. Yoga also recommends fasting as a means of purification and detoxification of the system. Fasting can be begin by missing one meal once a week, and then gradually increased to a whole day with a limited intake of milk and fruits as necessary. Certain guidelines should be followed while observing fasts.

1. Fix a specific day and meal to observe the fast and try to stay with that routine, e.g. miss lunch every Monday. This helps our body rhythms to adjust to the new routine.
2. Gradually, over a period of two to three months, extend the fasting to the entire day. If you are not able to observe

a complete fast, take some milk and fruits and adhere to that routine.

3. Fasting also has the effect of stimulating the subtler energies in the body, which lead to spiritual purification. While any degree of fasting, e.g. skipping a meal once a week, is sufficient to start the purification process, certain days of the year are especially important as the spiritual energy is more easily tapped on these days. As such these days are considered to be very auspicious and beneficial. Most of these days are decided on the basis of the traditional Indian calendar. It is a lunar based calendar which takes into consideration the astronomical configuration of the heavenly bodies, especially the moon and sun in relation to the earth. The most common and most beneficial of these days when fasting is prescribed are *Ekadashi*, or the eleventh day of the lunar fortnight (both the waxing as well as the waning fortnight) and *Maha Sivaratri*, or the thirteenth day of the dark fortnight in the month of Chaitra, which usually falls in February or March.

4. Devote some time of the day during the fast to mantra chanting and meditation. The body-mind is much more receptive during fasting and the effect of mantra and meditation is amplified during this time.

The dietary and nutritional requirements of each individual are different, especially so in case of illnesses like cancer, and there can be no hard and fast rules. However, yogic principles guide us in providing correct nutrition both to the body, mind and the causal aspects of our personality. This can be done in the form of a light sattwic diet with plenty of fresh fruits and vegetables, with minimal or no processed and animal foods. As well as providing nourishment on the physical level, a sattwic diet with plenty of fresh foods also ensures our diet is rich in pranic content. In addition, if the body permits, mild fasting (as in skipping one meal once a week or taking only fruits and milk once a week) on a regular basis increases pranic levels in the body.

19

Amaroli

Amaroli is the practice of consuming one's own urine in order to detoxify the body and develop immunity and vitality. Although initially, the idea may appear revolting and disgusting due to our social conditioning, we need to understand more about urine therapy before succumbing to negative associations. To understand the principles of amaroli, we need to take another look at the internal environment at the cellular level.

Life began on earth as a simple cell. Cells can survive only when specific physical characteristics for the environment outside the cells are met. Hence, the fluid environment surrounding the cell needs to be maintained within a very narrow range of these characteristics. However, primordial cells were subject to harsh external environmental factors which are detrimental to life. The life processes adapted to this situation by insulating themselves from this unviable external environment by creating their own internal environment.

In the course of evolution, life evolved from a single-celled organism to a multi-celled organism. It also created its own internal environment, which fostered survival by creating an internal sea of fluids in which all cells float and exist. This internal sea is an intermediary between the cell and the outer, external environment. It is fluid in nature and is 'external' to the cell – hence it is known as extra-cellular fluid. Extra-cellular fluid needs to maintain itself in a very strict, narrow range of various physical characteristics. If this narrow range is breached, cellular integrity is immediately at stake and cells degenerate rapidly outside these ranges.

Some of the important characteristics to be maintained are temperature, oxygen, carbon dioxide levels, acid-base balance, glucose levels and ionic balance. The body maintains these levels by filtering the blood in the kidneys. This involves subjecting the blood to the process of passive filtration across the cell membranes, passive reabsorption, active reabsorption in two stages and finally active secretion. At the end of this complex process, urine is formed. It is important to recognize that urine is a highly filtered derivative of blood and is sterile.

In addition, urine also contains many hormones, prostaglandins and other factors secreted or excreted by the kidneys, which are beneficial to the body. These factors promote healing, renormalization and regeneration. Ingestion of urine helps to re-introduce these factors into the body to promote healing and regeneration.

Our understanding of yogic physiology tells us that annamaya kosha, the physical dimension, is pervaded by five main pranic patterns. It is said that fusion of prana (the upward moving pranic pattern) and apana (the downward moving pranic pattern) results in unlocking the potential within each one of us, namely, awakening the latent kundalini energy. Apart from its obvious spiritual significance, this awakening has great healing and regenerative capacities. The entire potential of the pranas is then tapped, and this results in correcting the imbalances and defects of the pranic field in the body. All advanced yogic practices have this result.

The difficulty posed by these advanced yogic practices lies in mastering the ability to reverse the direction of flow of these two opposite moving pranic patterns, so that they meet in the centre. Amaroli is particularly powerful as it gives the individual a chance to achieve this very easily, literally without

127

any effort. The energy pattern responsible for formation of urine and its expulsion from the body is apana. As such, fresh urine is saturated with apanic energies. When ingested, it goes down the digestive tract, meeting the upward moving prana, and fusion takes place. This low scale and temporary fusion is sufficient to initiate healing changes in the body, which result in the reversal of pranic imbalances in the body, especially in affected parts. This causes a gradual reversal of the cancerous transformation in the body.

In addition, amaroli can also be used for local application directly on the tumour site. Compresses of fresh amaroli have been used to successfully revert active lesions to non-active lesions and then finally no lesions. Applications of amaroli compresses on the unbroken skin overlying the tumour mass has also been shown to be beneficial in managing cancer. Amaroli can thus be used in various forms in the management of cancer. It is advisable to discuss the practice of amaroli with a qualified yoga teacher/therapist.

3: Managing Cancer with Yoga

20

Cancer Management: A Practical Consideration

Yogic management of cancer can be conveniently divided into three main categories: preventive, corrective and palliative. Preventive means practising yoga to prevent the onset of cancer, which is feared due to the presence of risk factors, or due to the presence of early or precancerous lesions. This is the best time to begin practising yoga so that we can try to avoid the development of cancer.

The second category is corrective, i.e. practising yoga after the onset of cancer with the aim either of limiting, correcting or reversing the cancerous process. When combined with conventional medical therapy, yoga can operate as an adjunct, or it can help to reduce side effects. The modules described in the following chapters basically aim to help after the onset of cancer.

The third category is palliative practice, i.e. when the disease has progressed too far to be reversed. In such cases, the aim is to be able to spend the remainder of our time in a positive and healthy spirit, and to be able to pass on with dignity and minimal pain and suffering.

Yogic cancer management basically has five components, which are common to all three categories. The difference lies in the duration of time devoted to and the depth of the practices in each component. People coming in the preventive and palliative categories can devote as much time as they can allocate for yogic practices, although one to two hours a day is considered most beneficial. People in the second category should devote about three or four hours a day to these practices, as the priorities have radically altered and overcoming cancer now overrides everything else.

Yoga cancer management modules

Some modules of yogic practices are presented here to serve as guidelines for practising yoga in cancer management. Before beginning with these modules, it is important to emphasize that yogic practices should only be undertaken under the guidance of a trained yoga therapist. The precautions and contra-indications for each practice should be carefully observed (refer to *Asana Pranayama Mudra Bandha*, published by Yoga Publications Trust). If incorrectly performed, these practices can be counterproductive and do more harm than good. An abundance of common sense is perhaps the best companion. Give more emphasis to becoming comfortable in your practice and tuning in to your inner self, rather than going blindly into the practices. All practices should be matched to personal requirements.

Irrespective of your previous yoga experience, we recommend that you begin with the initial stages to receive the full benefits. There are five main components:
1. Shatkarmas or detoxification session (Duration: approximately 45 minutes)
2. Asana and pranayama session (Duration: approximately 60 minutes)
3. Yoga nidra and prana vidya session (Duration: approximately 45 minutes)
4. Visualization session (Duration: approximately 45 minutes)
5. Diet and lifestyle.

Cancer is a serious ailment, a manifestation of some serious imbalances within ourselves on multiple dimensions. Any program to manage these imbalances will have to be taken equally seriously to expect good results. The total period of time needed for all these sessions comes to around three and a half or four hours every day. While it is advisable to devote this amount of time to yoga practices to receive the full benefits, we realize that not everyone can do so because of other engagements. In such cases, we advise you to split the sessions into smaller units and modify them accordingly, in consultation with your yoga teacher. An alternative could be as follows:

1. Shatkarmas or detoxification session (Duration: approximately 45 minutes – on alternate days or twice a week)
2. Asana and pranayama session (Duration: approximately 30 minutes – with reduced number of rounds per practice and reduced number of practices)
3. Yoga nidra and prana vidya session (Duration: approximately 20 minutes. Yoga nidra and prana vidya can be practised for shorter durations according to individual need, and also during break times or while travelling.)
4. Visualization session (Duration: approximately 20 minutes. As with yoga nidra and prana vidya, visualization sessions can also be adapted easily to suit individual schedules.)
5. Diet and lifestyle.

The main emphasis is upon sensitizing our body-mind to the subtler forces within us and to trigger our latent healing capacities, so that we can use them to heal ourselves faster.

The modules in the next five chapters (chapters 21–25) are offered as standard therapeutic modules. For specific types of cancer, attention must be given to additional needs. Chapters 26–30 offer additional guidance for some of the most common types of cancers.

In addition to the usual precautions taken and prescribed for the specific case, the general emphasis in all types of cancers would be to:

1. Raise the pranic levels by consuming a diet rich in prana and using prana raising practices
2. Remove the blockages to the pranic flow by detoxification of the system through various asanas, pranayamas, amaroli and shatkarma procedures
3. Adopting a holistic, yogic diet and lifestyle
4. Strengthen the respective chakras by using the integrated yogic modules following

5. Emotional stabilization, expression and sublimation of suppressed thoughts, feelings and energy by using yoga nidra, introspection, and implementation of yama/niyama in the daily routine and use of the SWAN principle
6. Sublimate the unhealed emotions by practices of nada yoga, karma yoga and the adoption of some vedic and tantric practices according to the inclination of the individual. These include havan, mantra, yantra and mandala and are detailed in chapter 31
7. Help in harmonizing the neuroendocrine axis with use of appropriate visualization practices.

21

Session 1: Shatkarmas or Detoxification

In chapter, we explored the shatkarmas (six cleansing practices) and how they work to purify the being at different levels. The shatkarmas are:

- Neti, or nasal passage cleaning
- Dhauti, or cleaning of the gastrointestinal tract, including kunjal and shankhaprakshalana
- Basti, or colon cleansing
- Nauli kriya, or abdominal massaging
- Kapalbhati, or frontal passage cleaning
- Trataka, or fixed point gazing.

Shatkarmas should ideally be practised early in the morning on an empty stomach for maximum benefit. We recommend beginning the session at any convenient time between 4.30 am to 6.00 am. This period also corresponds with the traditional *brahmamuhurta*, a time considered to be auspicious as the mind and the body are fresh and receptive. The ideal body rhythms also coincide with this time. Starting the detoxification schedule at this time therefore ensures maximum effectiveness of the program.

The shatkarmas should be practised as follows:

1. **Om chanting**: Sit in any comfortable posture with the back straight and chant *Om* three times (denoting *Om* . . . nipresence, *Om* . . . niscience, *Om* . . . nipotence).
2. **Body awareness**: Continue sitting in the same posture and become aware of the body and breath. Rotate the

135

awareness from the top of the head to the toes two times. Now shift the awareness to the breath and become aware of the current of the breath, its rate, its rhythm and the movement of the body parts associated with the breath. (Duration: 1–2 minutes)

3. **Mind awareness**: Shift the awareness to the mind and become aware of the predominant emotions. Also become aware of the thoughts wandering across the mental screen. (Duration: 2 minutes)

4. **Detoxification practice**: A suitable and comfortable weekly regimen for detoxification is as follows:
Day 1: Jala neti
Day 2: Kunjal and jala neti
Day 3: Laghoo shankhaprakshalana, kunjal and jala neti
Day 4: Gap
Day 5: Jala neti
Day 6: Kunjal and jala neti
Day 7: Laghoo shankhaprakshalana, kunjal and jala neti.

5. **Shavasana**: At the end of the practice, lie down in shavasana and repeat stages 1 and 2 for 2 minutes each.

6. **Om chanting**: Finish the practice by chanting *Om* three times.

After following this routine for about eight weeks, the practices of agnisara kriya and nauli (depending on the proficiency level of the practitioner, health conditions and any other restrictions) can be gradually incorporated. These should be practised prior to neti, kunjal or laghoo shankha-prakshalana.

Basti should not be undertaken except under the supervision of a trained ayurvedic physician, as it requires an extraordinary amount of control over the anal and surrounding muscles, which is unlikely to be achieved by the patient. Kapalbhati and trataka are incorporated in the other sessions and hence need not be practised separately here.

136

22

Session 2: Asana and Pranayama

This session comprises asanas, pranayama, mudras and bandhas. The effect of these practices begins in the body, but culminates in the mind. They remove various physical and mental toxins which accumulate in the body and make the mind more receptive for the next set of mental practices.

Asanas tone the body, improve circulation and help us become attuned to our body's normal rhythms. They also regulate the neuro-endocrinal impulses, thereby helping transform stuck mental patterns. Pranayama aims to improve lung functioning at the organ level, and modifies cellular respiration and the effects of oxygen-carbon dioxide balance at the cellular level. These practices and how they work were discussed in detail in chapters 11 and 13.

This session has 12 modules designed so that the entire being, physical, mental and spiritual, undergoes a thorough yet gentle overhauling. This ensures that kinks and errors are gradually and surely replaced by appropriate and beneficial patterns. To derive the maximum benefit from this session, practise each step for 2 weeks before proceeding to the next step. The aim is not to achieve gymnastic flexibility in the body, but to sensitize the body-mind to the subtle force pervading it, to recognize its flow patterns and to align oneself with it.

Duration: The approximate duration of this session is about 60 minutes, of which 40 minutes is devoted to the various asanas, mudras and bandhas, while 15 minutes is devoted to the various pranayama practices.

Time of practice: These practices are best done on an empty stomach or about three hours after meals. As such, mid-morning is the most appropriate time for this session. One can have breakfast about 15 minutes after the first session (shatkarma), followed about three hours later by this session.

Sequence: Each asana practice should be performed 5 times on both sides, and also in a clockwise and anti-clockwise direction wherever applicable. At the end of each practice, close your eyes and become aware of the effect of the practice on your body, mind and emotions. Then practise one round mentally. The physical body remains perfectly stationary, but on the mental plane imagine that you are carrying out the practice.

Precautions and contra-indications: With pranayama practices, please note that while practising nadi shodhana pranayama, one must not use *antar kumbhaka* (internal breath retention) and *bahir kumbhaka* (external breath retention) in advanced malignancies. Breath retention should be done only after personal guidance from an expert yoga therapist. Kapalbhati is also contra-indicated in many types of cancer.

It is vital that these practices are begun only under appropriate guidance and after taking into consideration the contra-indications for each practice. These need to be evaluated on a case-by-case basis by an expert. At times, the malignancy is so advanced that only simple practices can be performed. In such conditions, it is important to know that an inability to perform physical postures can be corrected by practising other suitable yogic practices. The aim is not just physical flexibility, but to build a bridge between the body and mind so as to connect with the innate healing abilities latent within oneself. All these factors need to be taken into consideration before beginning the practices.

As a ready reference, a set of modules is presented below. Practise each module for at least two weeks before progressing to the next one.

Module I: a) Pawanmuktasana part 1
   b) Marjari-asana
   c) Vajrasana
   d) Tadasana, tiryaka tadasana, kati chakrasana
   e) Yogic breathing, bhramari pranayama
Module II: a) Pawanmuktasana part 1
   b) Makarasana
   c) Shashankasana
   d) Tadasana, tiryaka tadasana, kati chakrasana
   e) Nadi shodhana 1, bhramari pranayama
Module III: a) Pawanmuktasana part 1
   b) Bhujangasana
   c) Meru wakrasana
   d) Tadasana, tiryaka tadasana, kati chakrasana
   e) Simhasana, simhagarjanasana
   f) Nadi shodhana 2, bhramari pranayama
Module IV: a) Pawanmuktasana part 2
   b) Shashank bhujangasana
   c) Gomukhasana
   d) Surya namaskara postures – static
   e) Simhasana, simhagarjanasana
   f) Nadi shodhana 3, bhramari pranayama
Module V: a) Pawanmuktasana part 2
   b) Shashank bhujangasana
   c) Poorwa halasana
   d) Surya namaskara
   e) Simhasana, simhagarjanasana
   f) Nadi shodhana 3, ujjayi pranayama
Module VI: a) Pawanmuktasana part 2
   b) Vyaghrasana
   c) Poorwa halasana
   d) Surya namaskara with breath awareness
   e) Nadi shodhana 3, ujjayi pranayama
Module VII: a) Pawanmuktasana part 3
   b) Surya namaskara, 3 rounds
   c) Janu sirshasana/paschimottanasana
   d) Eka pada pranamasana

e) Siddha/siddha yoni asana

f) Nadi shodhana 4, kapalbhati pranayama

Module VIII: a) Pawanmuktasana part 3

    b) Surya namaskara, 3 rounds

    c) Janu sirshasana/paschimottanasana

    d) Vipareeta karani asana

    e) Ushtrasana/supta vajrasana

    f) Nadi shodhana 4, kapalbhati pranayama

Module IX: a) Pawanmuktasana part 3

    b) Surya namaskara, 3 rounds

    c) Vipareeta karani asana and 1 round of ushtrasana/ supta vajrasana

    d) Eka pada pranamasana

    e) Siddhasana/siddha yoni asana

    f) Nadi shodhana 4, kapalbhati, bhramari pranayama

Module X: a) Surya namaskara, 3 rounds

    b) Vipareeta karani asana and 1 round of ushtrasana/ supta vajrasana

    c) Eka pada pranamasana

    d) Ardha matsyendrasana

    e) Dhanurasana/saral shalabhasana

    f) Nadi shodhana 4, kapalbhati, bhramari pranayama

Module XI: a) Surya namaskara, 3 rounds

    b) Vipareeta karani asana and 1 round of ushtrasana/ supta vajrasana

    c) Eka pada pranamasana/natarajasana/garudasana

    d) Ardha matsyendrasana

    e) Dhanurasana/saral shalabhasana

    f) Nadi shodhana 4, kapalbhati, bhramari pranayama

Module XII: a) Surya namaskara, 3 rounds

    b) Vipareeta karani asana and 1 round of ushtrasana/ supta vajrasana

    c) Eka pada pranamasana/natarajasana/garudasana

    d) Ardha matsyendrasana

    e) Dhanurasana/saral shalabhasana

    f) Nadi shodhana 4, kapalbhati, bhramari pranayama.

23

Session 3: Yoga Nidra and Prana Vidya

This session comprises two main components dealing with yoga nidra, prana vidya and prana nidra. As discussed in chapter 14, yoga nidra is a practice of psychic relaxation. It brings to the surface and removes various subconscious samskaras, or deep-seated memories and impressions, which act as driving forces for the mind. It also relaxes the body, the mind and the psyche by removing unnecessary stimuli overloading the psychoneuroimmune apparatus.

Prana vidya and prana nidra invoke the pranic energy within us, helping us connect with the cosmic prana and thereby providing sufficient prana to the entire body. These pranas are consciously circulated all over the body and also directed especially to the tumour sites in which the prana is distorted and the levels are abysmally low. An increase in the pranic content at the site and all over the body helps in correcting the imbalances created, so that the disease process may be reversed. These practices were explained in more detail in chapters 11 and 14.

This session can be practised by one and all provided the restrictions for prana vidya practices are observed. It has the advantage of being applicable to all stages of malignancies and has no absolute contra-indications. This session is designed to last for about 45 minutes: 20 minutes for yoga nidra practice and the rest for prana vidya and prana nidra practice.

This session contains 20 modules, each of which should be practised for at least two weeks before proceeding to the next module. This is the minimum time needed for the awareness to attune itself to the degree of subtlety of the practices in each module and be ready to grasp the next set of practices. Undue haste in proceeding to the next module is not recommended as it would prove counterproductive. The session should be continued until one is comfortable with the practices taught in that module. Only then is it time to proceed to the next module. The duration of the session and the number of practices can be altered to suit individual needs in consultation with an expert yoga teacher. For details of prana vidya practices, refer to *Prana Pranayama Pranavidya*, a Yoga Publications Trust publication.

Module I: a) Yoga nidra 1
    b) Prana vidya: frontal passage, spinal passage
    c) Prana vidya: internal organ journey
Module II: a) Yoga nidra 2
    b) Prana vidya: siddhasana, moola bandha
    c) Prana vidya: chakra awareness, *Soham* awareness,
    d) Pranic bath (see chapter 14)
Module III: a) Yoga nidra 3
    b) Prana vidya: moola bandha, jalandhara, shambhavi
    c) Prana vidya: ida/pingala pathway, light corpuscles, five pranas visualization
    d) Pranic bath
Module IV: a) Yoga nidra 4
    b) Prana vidya: maha bandha, shambhavi mudra
    c) Prana vidya: practice 3, 4
    d) Pranic bath
Module V: a) Yoga nidra 4
    b) Prana vidya: maha bandha, khechari mudra, vipareeta karani mudra
    c) Prana vidya: 5, 6
    d) Pranic bath

Module VI: a) Yoga nidra 5

b) Prana vidya: maha bandha, khechari mudra, prana sanchalana

c) Prana vidya: 7, 8

d) Pranic bath

Module VII: a) Yoga nidra 5

b) Prana vidya: maha bandha, khechari mudra, pawan sanchalana

c) Prana vidya: practice 9, 10

d) Pranic bath

Module VIII a) Yoga nidra 5

b) Prana vidya: maha bandha, khechari mudra, shan-mukhi mudra

c) Prana vidya: practice 11, 12

d) Pranic bath

Module IX: a) Yoga nidra 5

b) Prana vidya: maha bandha, khechari mudra, chakra anusandhana

c) Prana vidya: practice 13, 14

d) Pranic bath

Module X: a) Yoga nidra 5

b) Prana vidya: maha bandha, khechari mudra, shambhavi mudra, prana sanchalana

c) Prana vidya: practice 15, 16

d) Pranic bath

Module XI: a) Yoga nidra 5

b) Prana vidya: maha bandha, khechari mudra, shambhavi mudra, prana sanchalana

c) Prana vidya: practice 17, 18

d) Pranic bath

Module XII: a) Yoga nidra 5

b) Prana vidya: maha bandha, khechari mudra, shambhavi mudra, prana sanchalana

c) Prana vidya: practice 19, 20

d) Pranic bath.

143

24

Session 4: Guided Imagery or Meditation

An untrained mind is like a wild horse or elephant, so powerful it can destroy our stability and peace in the twinkling of an eye. This strength is, however, a dissipated and misdirected energy, of no use to us in this form. Some thoughts take root in an untrained mind and lead us to despair. This is very true especially in cancer patients. Meditative practices or guided imagery practices help us to befriend the mind and train it so that this raw energy can be effectively harnessed for healing purposes.

To begin with, we should become aware of any visual sensations or images which spontaneously pop up on our mental screen. Neutral objects (those objects which do not evoke any strong and powerful emotional reactions within us) which we have seen earlier in life can be incorporated as a next step in training the mind to retain the visual image seen. Then we should attempt to integrate the other senses such as sound, smell, touch, taste and thoughts with the visualizations. As we become familiar with these practices we should move on to evoking specific thoughts and playing them out on our mental screens with complete audio-visual effects! Incorporating positive healing thoughts and visualizations is included in this session.

These practices have a manifold effect. Each one is able to evoke latent memories and suppressed associations deep from our unconscious and helps us to let them play themselves out harmlessly without actually manifesting them physically. This helps to release the energy locked in that thought complex or samskara, and also helps us create more positive and helpful mental patterns. These have a deep impact on the neurohormonal state of our body, as well as the ability to boost the functioning of the various protective mechanisms in our being at all levels, including mental and spiritual.

Each module has three basic components designed to activate and channel the mental energies. Trataka is a practice to concentrate the dissipated tendencies of the mind, while body awareness and other pratyahara practices help to channel the mental energies towards specific goals.

The visualizations then allow us to play out various scenes in the mind, which helps to cleanse the unconscious mind of various samskaras or associations from past experiences. Visualization can begin with imagining and recreating simple objects which have already been seen earlier in life, e.g. a dog, a cat, a tree, a red rose, a burning flame and so on. We then proceed to let the mind come up with any idea or thought spontaneously and then to watch it unfold in the mind.

Once the mind is sufficiently trained, we can move to the next stage, which is suggesting a specific event to the mind and recreating the entire sequence of events as if they were actually taking place. Having trained the mind this far, we then suggest specific thoughts or events to the mind which have a positive prognostic bearing on our disease, e.g. visualizing the tumour shrinking in size, or visualizing an upcoming chemotherapy or radiotherapy session, and seeing the side effects as much reduced, etc. This way we can systematically train our mind to respond in a specific fashion which increases the efficiency of the body-mind to combat the disease.

Module I: a) Trataka
   b) Body awareness, kaya sthairyam
   c) Simple object visualizations
Module II: a) Trataka
   b) Antar mouna 1
   c) Simple object visualizations
Module III: a) Trataka
   b) Antar mouna 2
   c) Extended object visualizations
Module IV: a) Trataka
   b) Antar mouna 2
   c) Event visualizations
Module V: a) Trataka
   b) Antar mouna 3
   c) Spontaneous thought visualizations
Module VI: a) Trataka
   b) Antar mouna 3
   c) Specific thought visualizations
Module VII: a) Trataka
   b) Antar mouna 4
   c) Prognostic thought visualizations
Module VIII: a) Trataka
   b) Antar mouna 4
   c) Chidakasha dharana 1
Module IX: a) Trataka
   b) Antar mouna 5
   c) Chidakasha dharana 2
Module X: a) Trataka
   b) Antar mouna 5
   c) Chidakasha dharana 3
Module XI: a) Trataka
   b) Antar mouna 6
   c) Chidakasha dharana 4
Module XII: a) Trataka
   b) Antar mouna 6
   c) Chidakasha dharana 4.

25

Session 5: Diet and Lifestyle

Although diet and lifestyle is being presented in a session format, it must be remembered that in reality, this session extends throughout the whole day and continues from day to day. Due to earlier preset habits, the changes suggested here might, at first, seem a little difficult to incorporate into our lives. This process should be gradual and smooth to avoid any distress to an already overloaded system. This session integrates the activities of diet, nada yoga, karma yoga and dynamic meditation practices.

Diet, as we have seen, has two basic components: physical and subtle. On a physical level we need to have a good nutritious diet, containing sufficient natural fruits and vegetables. On a subtle level, the diet has to be sattwic or pure with some rajasic or stimulating components. Tamasic or unhealthy components should be scrupulously avoided. Attention should also be given to our thoughts as they provide nutrition to the mind, which performs a crucial role in activating and maintaining the healing powers of the inner self.

Some important dietary pointers
- Eat at fixed meal times, trying to synchronize them with sunrise, noon and sunset whenever possible.
- Eat fresh food, preferably home cooked – a sattwic diet.
- Try to grow some vegetables, salads and fruits for yourself.
- Increase the dietary fibre content.

- Fast completely at least once a week, and on Ekadashi, the eleventh day of the lunar fortnight (both waxing and waning).
- Stop/minimize eating meat products and processed foods.
- Maintain a light-hearted atmosphere while eating.
- Avoid watching TV during meal times.

Lifestyle

How we live affects the way we feel and think, and this has a subtle effect on the entire body physiology. Today, we have moved far away from nature and her rhythms. However, our bodies still function on the same lines as they always have. This creates disharmony on a very subtle plane. The body rhythms become disturbed, distorted and finally blocked, leading to various illnesses, including cancer. The aim is to rediscover our natural rhythms and get them flowing. To do this, we need to make various changes in ourselves. It is much easier for the body and mind to shift gradually into a newer pattern than remain in the one they have been exposed to and to which they have adapted (with whatever compromises). This can be done by incorporating the practices bit by bit. Some important pointers are:

- Start amaroli externally, then internally.
- Choose one of the yamas/niyamas and gradually begin to incorporate that value into your life. First reflect, introspect and grasp the true significance of the particular yama or niyama. Next, analyze how it can become part of your life without causing upheavals, and then gradually cultivate that particular yama/niyama in the way you live.
- Adopt the SWAN principle. SWAN is a simple, effective lifestyle analysis matrix formulated by Swami Niranjan-ananda. It helps us to incorporate spiritual principles in our practical day-to-day lives. SWAN is an acronym for **S**trength, **W**eakness, **A**mbition, **N**eed. Each of us has certain attributes under each of these headings. We need to build up our strong points and use them to balance our weaknesses. Next we have to identify and work upon our

148

weaknesses, so as to improve ourselves and not fall into the rut of self-castigation. Having done this, we need to identify, analyze and then set out to achieve our ambitions and aspirations. To maintain a proper perspective of the ground reality, we also have to know our needs and see to it that we fulfil them.

This simple analysis helps us to understand our priorities and liabilities. It also helps us manage our lives in a much more organized and effective manner.

- Take up any of the following according to choice and inclination, and practise it as a hobby for some period of time daily:
  - instrumental music
  - vocal music singing
  - painting
  - sculpting
  - carving
  - sketching
  - writing.
- Start taking a morning and evening walk if possible.
- Take up gardening.
- Do some selfless charitable work, no matter how small.
- Spend at least 10–15 minutes with your family or friends in laughter, sharing jokes and anecdotes.
- Adopt a pet (keeping in mind practical considerations about the pet too!).
- Give up smoking and alcohol.

These yogic principles need to be fitted in according to the situation of the individual, with particular regard to the type of cancer and each person's condition. To assist in developing a better understanding, chapters 26–30 deal with some common types of cancer and their yogic analysis. This should form the basis of managing cancer through yoga.

26

Oropharyngeal Cancer

The oropharynx is a tubular structure lined on all sides by muscles. It extends from the mouth back towards the oesophagus. The commonest type of cancer afflicting this region is squamous cell carcinoma, which usually affects the lips, tongue, cheeks and pharynx. It is caused by repetitive injury or chronic irritation to the lining. The commonest causes are cigarette smoking, chewing tobacco and drinking alcohol. In India and parts of Asia, chewing betel nut is another important cause.

The oral cavity and pharynx serve as the receptor site for food, water and air into the body. The tonsils and Waldeyer's ring on the pharyngeal walls act as the first immune barrier for the food, water and air which enters the system from these openings. The lips, cheeks, teeth, tongue and the various salivary glands help in the processing of food. These are all lined by a sensitive stratified epithelium (multi-layered lining). Any carcinogenic irritants entering the body first come into contact with this lining, making it more susceptible to injury and disease. Smoking and tobacco and/or betel nut chewing act as prolonged irritants to this lining, which then gradually undergoes the cancerous transformation.

On a pranic level, this area is the entry portal of external prana into the body. Hence, it is an important point for filtering unwanted, harmful pranic activity and accepting beneficial and useful pranic energy.

In yoga, the mouth and neck, in general, are regulated by vishuddhi chakra, which deals with communication and purification. Dysfunctions in vishuddhi cause communication problems, difficulties in accepting situations and an inability to remove toxic matter entering via this portal. If it becomes chronic (meaning recurrent or long-lasting), it is strongly unbalancing. A strong feedback mechanism starts in which one impulse results in another impulse of a higher intensity recurring at progressively shorter intervals and giving rise to a chain reaction of such events. This can lead to disastrous and lethal effects, and over a period of time a cancerous lesion can manifest in the corresponding organs. Chronic irritants such as cigarette smoke, pollution and other similar factors compound the situation and hasten the manifestation of oropharyngeal cancer.

The disease commonly manifests as a small nodule, a non-healing ulcer or recurrent injury (such as a sharp tooth irritating the mucosa) in the oral cavity, either on the cheeks, gums, tongue or pharyngeal walls. The common characteristics are:

1. Ulcerates and is non-healing in nature
2. Keeps growing in size
3. May present as a non-healing irritant, dry cough
4. Foul smelling in nature.

If unchecked, the disease invades the local tissues and also spreads to distant sites.

Local spread: To the surrounding oral cavity tissues, including the overlying skin and deeper structures such as the muscles, glands and bones in the oropharyngeal cavity.

Lymphatic spread: To submandibular glands, neck glands (anterior and posterior sternocleido mastoid lymph nodes) and supraclavicular lymph nodes.

Distant spread: To the liver, lungs and brain.

Important risk factors

The probability of contracting disease has been seen to be higher if the following risk factors exist.

At annamaya kosha level – modifiable risk factors:
1. Environmental factors:
   - Exposure to environmental pollutants
   - Occupational hazards due to exposure to lead, arsenic and other carcinogens.
2. Host factors:
   - Cigarette smoking
   - Tobacco/ betel nut/betel leaf chewing
   - Prolonged alcohol intake.

At pranamaya kosha level:
1. Blockages to the pranic flow, especially the sub-pranas udana and samana
2. Chronic depletion of pranas in the head and neck region
3. Chakras affected: anahata, vishuddhi, mooladhara.

At manomaya kosha level – The presence of mental carcinogens in the form of:
1. Recurrent brooding thoughts
2. Difficulties in expressing thoughts and emotions
3. Emotional neglect by parents or society, giving rise to low self-esteem, guilt complexes, fears and phobias
4. Inappropriate aggressive tendencies
5. High levels of mental stress, chronic stress.

Aim of treatment

In addition to the standard therapeutic modules discussed in chapters 20–25, attention must be given to emotional requirements. Vishuddhi is related to communication and expression. Blockages in these areas need to be examined and activities which reinforce good communication need to be implemented.

Important contra-indications

The practices of kunjal, nauli and kapalbhati are contra-indicated in oropharyngeal cancers, unless evaluated by a medical professional and a yoga therapist.

27

Lung Cancer

Lung cancer is one of the leading causes of cancer deaths. The lungs are among the most important and vital organs in the body. Their primary function is to take in atmospheric air, separate the oxygen component, absorb it into the system and pass it to the circulatory system via the blood to be distributed to the tissues in the body. At the same time, the lungs also remove carbon dioxide and other metabolic end products which are potentially harmful to the body, returning them to the atmosphere.

Each and every cell of the body needs oxygen to carry out the various chemical reactions necessary for energy production. Without this, the cell cannot survive. As the metabolic end product of its activities, it produces carbon dioxide, which is detrimental to cell health if it accumulates in the body. Hence, a regular supply of oxygen and removal of carbon dioxide and other products from the cell is imperative. This is done by the circulatory system with the help of the lungs, which act as filters to separate and take in oxygen from the air and release metabolic end products, primarily carbon dioxide, back into the air.

On the pranic level, the lungs act as the main organs for absorbing prana from the air (note that prana should not be confused with oxygen). The prana thus absorbed is distributed all over the body and manages the body's activities in conjunction with prana generated by the body.

The lungs, therefore, act as providers of pranic energy in the body.

According to yoga, the lungs and the respiratory system in general are regulated by anahata chakra, which deals with feelings of love and compassion, and vishuddhi chakra, which deals with communication and purification. Dysfunctions in these aspects of the personality can naturally be expected to manifest through the organs controlled by these chakras. In today's society love is a most misunderstood and also a most sought after entity. When there is a major dysfunction in understanding and manifesting love, communication and assimilation problems are inevitable. These factors are compounded by other general factors and can play an important role in managing lung cancer.

Cigarette smoking, environmental factors such as exposure to carcinogenic chemicals and industrial pollutants, exposure to radiation and genetic factors are risk factors for lung cancer. Causative host factors include chronic pranic depletion due to improper breathing techniques or long-standing dysfunctions in either receiving love or expressing love, communication blocks, excessive emotional repression, a depressive brooding nature and long-standing nutritional imbalances.

Important risk factors

The probability of contracting disease has been seen to be higher if the following risk factors exist.

At annamaya kosha level:
1. Non-modifiable risk factors:
   • Hereditary: history of the disease process in the family.
2. Modifiable risk factors:
   • Cigarette smoking
   • Sedentary lifestyle
   • High levels of mental stress.

At pranamaya kosha level:
1. Blockages to pranic flow, especially the sub-types prana and samana
2. Chronic depletion of pranas in the chest region

3. Chakras affected: anahata, vishuddhi, mooladhara and swadhisthana
4. Nadis involved: predominant blockage or associated difficulty of expression of ida nadi and the left swara.

At manomaya kosha level:
The presence of mental carcinogens in the form of:
1. Non-acceptance of life's situations
2. Wanting to withhold or block the expression of certain thought patterns (which are felt to be inappropriate yet keep surfacing to the mind)
3. Brooding over past tensions – not releasing or letting them go can create difficulties in bringing in and assimilating newer ideas. This can lead to blockages in the chakras mentioned above.
4. While sex-related topics are no longer taboo today, a complete and harmonized integration of sexual issues is not common, which leads to a host of subtle mental complexes. This can cause difficulties in expression and acceptance and letting go of viewpoints, which may contribute to lung cancer.

Aim of treatment
In addition to the standard therapeutic modules discussed in chapters 20–25, attention must be given to being flexible and gaining the ability to adapt to newer situations, which counters the problems of holding on or not letting go.

Important contra-indications
Kunjal, nauli and kapalbhati are contra-indicated in lung cancer, unless evaluated by a medical professional and a yoga therapist.

28

Breast Cancer

Breast cancer is the most common type of cancer in women. In addition to other aspects of malignancies affecting the body, breast cancer evokes a strong emotional response as it affects a very intimate part of one's body, personality and personal identification. This can make breast cancer a particularly traumatic experience. A brief sketch of some important aspects of the yogic management of breast cancer is outlined below.

Usually, the disease manifests as a small lump in the breast. Due to the rapid, disorganized growth pattern, the nodule shows the following characteristics:

1. Growth in size is usually rapid
2. Surface of the lump is usually uneven rather than smooth
3. Consistency is usually hard
4. The lump is not usually freely mobile in the breast
5. The nipple of the affected breast may have recently become inverted
6. Appearance of watery, mucoid or bloody discharge from the nipple
7. Ulceration of the skin overlying the lump
8. The later appearance of nodes in the armpit/s.

If unchecked, the disease invades local tissues and also spreads to distant sites.

Local spread: To surrounding breast tissue, overlying skin, underlying muscles of the chest wall, ribs, lungs and the opposite breast.

Lymphatic spread: To the nodes in the armpit, and to other surrounding lymph nodes such as those located within the chest.

Via blood vessels: To the liver, lungs, bone and brain.

Important risk factors

The probability of contracting disease has been seen to be higher if the following risk factors exist.

At annamaya kosha level:

1. Non-modifiable risk factors:
   - Presence of breast cancer in close relatives, particularly when more than one relative is affected or when affected at a young age.
   - Certain ovarian cancers within the family can increase the risk of breast cancer.
   - Early menarche (onset of the menstrual cycle)
   - Late menopause
   - Nulliparity (when a woman has not borne any children)
   - Advanced age for the first pregnancy.
2. Modifiable risk factors:
   - Obesity
   - Tobacco smoking.

At pranamaya kosha level:

1. Blockages to the pranic flow, especially the sub-types prana and samana
2. Chronic depletion of pranas in the chest region
3. Chakras affected: anahata, vishuddhi, mooladhara and swadhisthana
4. Nadis involved: predominant blockage or associated difficulty of expression of ida nadi and the left swara.

At manomaya kosha level – The presence of mental carcinogens in the form of:

1. Recurrent brooding thoughts, especially related to sexuality
2. Suppression of the maternal instinct
3. Emotional neglect by parents or society, leading to low self-esteem, guilt complexes, fears and phobias

157

4. Inappropriate aggressive tendencies which may suppress the creative and aesthetic side of the personality.

Aim of treatment

In addition to the standard therapeutic modules discussed in chapters 20–25, suppressed emotional needs and their expression with varying degrees of selflessness is especially important as it is the predominant attribute of the chakras associated with breast cancer.

29

Colorectal Cancer

The large intestines carry out the important function of completing the absorption of food after most of the absorption has taken place in the small intestines. Their main role is to absorb water and carry non-absorbed food and other waste matter out as faeces into the rectum and anal canal so that it can be excreted.

On the mental or manomaya dimension, this region, especially the rectum and anal canal, are intimately related to many impressions formed in early childhood in association with toilet training. Difficulties and phobias associated with toilet training have been implicated in many psychological abnormalities manifesting in adult life. If these complexes are not resolved and continue to fester beneath the surface, they may contribute to the manifestation of cancer, especially of the colon, rectum and anal canal.

Cancer of the large intestines ranks closely behind lung cancer and is the second most common cause of death due to cancer. Cancer of the colorectal region usually manifests with non-specific complaints such as:

- Change in the usual bowel habits
- Loss of weight for no obvious reason
- Anaemia (manifesting as pale skin, tiredness and breath-lessness)
- Blood in stools

- Abdominal cramping
- Obstructed bowel movements.

Diagnosis is established using imaging techniques to visualize the lining of the intestines and is confirmed by biopsy.

Important risk factors

The possibility of developing bowel cancer has been seen to be higher if the following risk factors exist.

At annamaya kosha level:

1. Non-modifiable factors:
   - Hereditary: family history of colorectal cancer
   - Certain intestinal polyps, inflammatory bowel disease
   - Type 2 diabetes mellitus.
2. Modifiable risk factors:
   - Alcohol
   - Smoking
   - Sedentary lifestyle
   - Dietary factors: as discussed in chapters 5, 18 and 25 on diet and nutrition, in particular:
     a) Prolonged low fibre content in the diet
     b) High red meat content, especially processed meat
     c) Obesity
     d) Sedentary lifestyle.

At pranamaya kosha level:

1. Blockages to the pranic flow, especially the sub-types samana and apana
2. Chronic depletion of pranas in the abdominal region
3. Chakras affected: manipura, mooladhara and swadhi-sthana

At manomaya kosha level – The presence of mental carcinogens in the form of:

1. recurrent brooding thoughts
2. inappropriate expression of insecurities, attachments and desires, especially in close interpersonal relationships
3. fear of loss of possession of material objects and belongings
4. chronic high levels of mental tension.

160

Aim of treatment

In addition to the standard therapeutic modules discussed in chapters 20–25, attention must be given to chronic mental stress and tension, the ability to purge ideas and values which have lost their utility and to 'let go' of them. Sharing what is ours with other people we do not consider to be 'ours' is also an important feature to be inculcated for optimal benefits. In addition to dietary modification, these are the most important factors to deal with in managing colorectal cancer.

30

Skin Cancer

Skin cancer is increasingly common for many reasons such as the prevalence of environmental pollutants, industrial wastes, wide scale use of chemicals on the skin as cosmetics and exposure to ultraviolet radiation. The greatest risk factor is exposure to the sun. Important points to be borne in mind while managing skin cancer are outlined below. The usual manifestations of skin cancer vary, depending on the location of the lesion. The most common symptoms are a rapidly growing nodule which ulcerates and forms a non-healing ulcer. The diagnosis is established by biopsy.

Important risk factors
The possibility of contracting the disease has been seen to be higher if the following risk factors exist.
At annamaya kosha level:
1. Non-modifiable factors:
   • Genetic predisposition
   • Being male
   • Fair complexion
   • Multiple moles
   • Some inheritable conditions like xeroderma pigmentosum
   • Reduced immunity (such as due to HIV infection or long term use of certain medications).

2. Modifiable risk factors:
   - Exposure to ultraviolet radiation (which has increased due to the thinning of the ozone layer), particularly blistering sunburn in childhood
   - Smoking
   - Exposure to carcinogenic chemicals such as arsenic, lead, coal tar products, and so on.

At pranamaya kosha level:
1. Blockages to the pranic flow, especially the sub-types vyana and samana
2. Chronic depletion of the pranas
3. Chakras affected: manipura, anahata, mooladhara and swadhisthana.

Aim of treatment

In addition to the standard therapeutic modules discussed in chapters 20–25, attention must be given to managing issues of individual identity, limitations and presentation, which can have a bearing on the skin, in addition to chronic mental stress and tension, and dietary factors.

31

Vedic and Tantric Practices for Cancer Management

In the quest to manage cancer we have looked at yogic practices and their therapeutic aspects. This chapter explores vedic and tantric principles which can be beneficial in the management of cancer.

The most important points are:

- Using the fire element to transcend the mind and connect to higher dimensions of existence. This includes performing havans and yajnas.
- Harnessing the power of sound to invoke cosmic forces for individual purposes. This includes practising mantras and nada yoga.
- Using certain specific geometric formations, known as yantras, to focus and strengthen the mind.
- Using various forms and shapes to fulfil emotional needs while providing a channel for their constructive utilization. Mandalas are used for this purpose.

Yoga has freely borrowed concepts from these principles and integrated them within its system. When used in the right combinations and in the correct manner, they are extremely beneficial, as they deal with the deeper psychological framework of the individual. We shall concentrate on the triad of mantra, yantra and mandala, and the process of yajna or havan.

Mantra, yantra and mandala

Mantras are sound packets of specific frequencies which correspond to the innate vibrations of various inner body parts and chakras. Repetition of such mantras brings about a profound change in a person's mental, emotional and physical status. As mantra is an integral part of Indian mythology and also has an important bearing on various religious scriptures and practices, it has been misunderstood as having religious meanings and has been associated with religious dogma. For example, in yoga it is understood that the syllables in the mantra *Om Namah Shivaya* correspond to particular chakras and repeating this mantra stimulates those chakras, bringing about physiological and psychic changes in the personality. The specific cosmic force invoked by this mantra, also known as the presiding deity of the mantra, is said to bless the person repeating it.

To understand this concept in a more modern context, take the example of a mobile phone. A mobile phone needs to be activated if one is to use it. Then the user needs to deposit a pre-paid amount to ensure sufficient talk time. Once this is done, the user can access the mobile phone facilities and communicate with others easily. The mantra is like the instructions about activation. The specifications of mantra practice are like the details of this process. Proficiency leads to activation of the chakras, which help us tune in to a higher realm of existence. The rules of mantra practice are like the talk time deposit and safety regulations. On successfully completing the entire process, we can tap into this subtler dimension of existence and achieve many 'miracles', in the same way as the mobile user performs a 'miracle' by communicating with a person many thousands of miles away without physically moving even an inch.

For the emotionally inclined, the higher force is felt to be propitiated by practising this 'activation' mantra and being pleased, he or she bestows the boon of distant communication on the user. Some common mantras are given in Appendix 2.

Yantras, on the other hand, have a direct psychological bearing on the deep unconscious. Yantras are geometric patterns which trigger off changes in the unconscious mind and bring about changes in consciousness. The commonest method of using a yantra is in conjunction with a mantra. By practising trataka on the yantra, it becomes a tool for concentrating the mind. Drawing or painting the yantra and placing images of yantras in the home are also recommended. Some common yantras are given in Appendix 3.

These practices, by virtue of tapping the higher levels of our personality, vijnanamaya and anandamaya koshas, can bring about miraculous healing changes. Christ, who is attributed with healing the sick and performing miracles like reviving the dead, was an accomplished yogi. His miraculous healing powers indicate that he had been able to awaken the higher koshas, and that his anahata, vishuddhi and ajna chakras were activated. There have been many healers throughout history who have routinely performed many such 'miracles', as they had been able to activate their higher chakras which impart such abilities.

Yajna and havan

Fire is an element of transformation. When prehistoric man came into contact with fire, his consciousness made a quantum leap and he rose from animal status to human status with the ability to influence his surroundings. The same principle is utilized for therapeutic purposes. Yajnas and havans incorporate the use of mantras, fire, herbs and certain codes of conduct to achieve this. By using a simple healing mantra like the Mahamrityunjaya mantra, the action of the mantra can be invoked in conjunction with the effect of fire on the psyche and the effect of the herbs on the surroundings.

When faced with cancer, not only does our body suffer, but our mind, emotions and psyche also take a deep battering. The patient can fall into a vicious circle of despondency, gloom and despair which negatively affects their health. In addition, these feelings can affect the 'vibe' or feeling of their

166

surroundings. Yajnas and havans are a simple means by which one can break this vicious circle and instil a sense of peace, purpose and hope within oneself and the surroundings.

There are many types of yajnas and havans which can be performed for better health and to invoke the subtler powers governing nature. These can be elaborate and ritualistic, but can also be performed in a simple manner by concentrating more on the mantra and the offering to the fire. Both yield similar results. More information on this subject is available in *Yajna, A Comprehensive Survey*, published by Yoga Publications Trust.

32

People Dying with Cancer

Everyone born on this earth has to die. There is no exception to this stark rule of life. In fact, the Indian scriptures mention that the four events of birth, death, old age and disease are closely interrelated, and that one cannot exist without the other. Our society has prepared us for life and takes care (or at least tries to take care) of our requirements in disease and old age. However, it has left us to fend for ourselves in facing the hardest one of all – death.

Death comes to all and very often its harbinger is illness and old age. When struck by cancer, a life-threatening disease, we are catapulted into the face of death at close quarters. Yoga provides a way to walk away from death and learn a few lessons in the process. Yoga also offers assistance to those in whom the disease has gone too far to be reversed or managed.

In yoga, acceptance is the first step in reaching our goal. The same principle can also help people who are terminally ill. As we approach death, yoga helps us to maintain our dignity and quality of life. It also helps us manage our emotions and feelings, come to terms with our desires and provides an opportunity to set priorities with equanimity. It helps us attain the clear-headed perception needed to make strong decisions and stick to them. Most importantly, it hands us the key to remain joyful and happy no matter what happens. These feelings and emotions need not be dependent on external circumstances as society has taught us to believe.

Rather, the absence of joy and happiness comes from unbalanced states of mind which occur due to our identification with the external at the expense of our inner life. Acceptance prepares us to meet the reality beyond the body, whether we call it God, supreme consciousness, karmic forces or any other name we feel comfortable with.

Yoga and the purpose of life

Death raises stubborn questions about life, its purpose and about our sense of individuality and identity. With death staring us in the face, there is nowhere to hide, nothing to distract the mind from such questions. These final moments can be utterly devastating and heart wrenching. It is in these moments that our entire life flashes before us. All our desires, unfulfilled dreams, ambitions and passions come up and there is an increasing sense of futility. One may feel lost and unable to fathom the apparent injustice meted out. "When there are so many things to be done, so much pain and suffering, how can it be that I am to die?" is a common refrain felt and expressed. There seems to be no purpose in life. All that we have done in our life suddenly seems so insignificant and useless. Anger, fear, hatred and helplessness are the most common emotions to surface.

Yoga considers the individual person to be an individual spark of the cosmic divinity. This individual spark of consciousness is known as the *jivatma*. It is a passenger in the triad of the body-mind-spirit, which can be likened to a vehicle, horses, driver and passenger. The passenger in the vehicle, changes the vehicle, the body, when it becomes old and full of defects. Such a vehicle can no longer serve the passenger's purpose and hence the passenger simply changes vehicles. Just as we change our old clothes and replace them with new ones, similarly, the jivatma or individual changes bodies and replaces an old worn out body with a brand new one more suited to its purpose! When we are able to identify with the jivatma, not the body, the whole paradigm shifts, and we gain a greater understanding of the difficult yet

169

valuable questions which may haunt us about the purpose of life.

Such questions form the basis of one stream of yoga – *jnana yoga*, the yoga of intuitive knowledge and wisdom. Jnana refers specifically to higher knowledge of the *atman*, the spirit, the soul, the self beyond body and mind, the indweller present in each one of us. 'Who am I?' 'Am I the body, the mind, the emotions or am I something beyond these too?' 'If I am the atman, then why do I not experience it?' 'What is the nature of the atman?' Every practitioner of jnana yoga ponders on these questions.

Atman is the subject of experience, not intellectualization. However, we need to make a beginning somewhere. So firstly, we should try to know more about the atman, or higher reality. This can be done by listening to wise people who have such knowledge or by reading on the subject, and then assimilating this knowledge and pondering on it. As we think more and more about it, we develop deeper insights into the subject. Gradually we delve deeper and draw more and more from our own experiences and understanding. This leads to the mind being concentrated on the atman, which leads us to a greater and experiential knowledge of the atman.

In the present context, these self-analytical practices help us gain our bearings, not only in relation to the body, but in relation to the atman, or *purusha* or pure consciousness, dwelling within us, and help us gain a better acceptance of the situation.

In addition to the yogic practices suggested in the cancer management modules, the reading of spiritual texts such as the *Bhagavad Gita*, *Ramayana*, Upanishads, Bible, Koran and others is recommended. These texts offer a glimpse of understanding into this utterly complicated world and the mysterious ways in which it works. Singing bhajans, kirtan and other joyful music is also a very useful means of uplifting the emotions, and gives us courage to walk to the end.

We can also learn by reflecting on the lives of illustrious spiritual luminaries who were affected by cancer. Paramahamsa Ramakrishna had cancer of the throat. Often the pain would be excruciating and his disciples would worry about him and beg him to do something. His calm reply was, "It is the body which is affected, why let my mind be agitated by that? My mind is fixed on the lotus feet of the Divine Mother. I experience her presence even more strongly now."

Ramana Maharshi had cancer in his arms. He did not let that disturb his routine or his life. At the insistence of his disciples he assented to undergo surgery, but commented that what has to happen will come to pass. Why waste any energy on it? This body is after all just a garb. It is bound to fall off some time or other. He maintained his equanimity and poise even in death.

The lives of such souls can serve as examples for us. They did not consider death to be a frightening experience. It was simply the end of a chapter for them. The story of life continues in the next chapter.

A combination of yogic practices – asana, pranayama, yoga nidra and meditation – practised judiciously can help a person prepare for an inevitable and impending death. These practices help us come to terms with the finality of death and the possibility of meeting the Creator with a calm and serene mind.

33

A List of Asanas and Pranayamas

The following is a brief introduction to the asana and prana-yama practices included in chapter 22. For more detailed and specific instructions, including sequence of practices, precautions, contra-indications and benefits, refer to *Asana Pranayama Mudra Bandha*, *Prana Pranayama Prana Vidya* and *Yoga and Kriya*, published by Yoga Publications Trust. It is important to note that all these practices need to be learned from a trained yoga therapist who understands the circumstances of the person with cancer and can customize the practices accordingly. The prescribed practices should be learnt under direct supervision and guidance.

Pawanmuktasana 1, 2 and 3
The pawanmuktasana series is by far the most important group of practices, and forms the foundation of our yogic journey. These practices open up all the major joints of the body, and work on each joint systematically. The philosophy of ayurveda, dealing with the science of healthy living, describes three basic humours in the body: *kapha* (mucus), *pitta* (bile) and *vata* (wind). According to ayurveda, most diseases have a strong element of vata derangement. Vata has a great propensity to localize in and around the joints, perhaps because vata signifies movement, and in the physical body, movements are centred around the joints.

The pawanmuktasana practices deal with all the important joints and all the movements possible by each joint. This group of asanas also remove blockages in the energy pathways. Such blockages can be caused by bad posture, psychological or emotional blockages, or an unbalanced lifestyle. An accumulation of muscular tension, stiffness and functional defects gradually develops due to these blockages. If this occurs over a long period of time, structural damage may result. The next logical effect is changes in the genetic structure, either due to these defects or as a result of the body's effort to counter these continued disturbances to the internal environment. We have already seen that cancer is a cumulative disorder in which genetic changes (mutations) bring about changes in the fundamentals of cellular behaviour. The pawanmuktasana series of asanas is an important link to block as well as reverse the build-up to these changes.

The pawanmuktasana series, like all other asanas, acts primarily by relaxing and balancing the mind and tuning up the hormonal secretions, the autonomic nervous system, and the activities of the internal organs. This effect is accentuated by the integration of breath synchronization and mental awareness with the physical movements. The pawanmukt-asana series is divided into three groups: part 1 loosens up the joints of the body, part 2 strengthens the digestive system and part 3 improves the energy flow in the body.

Effects on the joints
Let us take the example of a specific joint – the ankle joint, a modified ball and socket joint. It is said to be a hinge joint; however, it also has some rotational ability. Movements possible with this joint are:
1. Flexion – extension (i.e. forward and backward movement)
2. Inversion – eversion (turning the sole inwards and outwards)
3. Rotation, which is actually a combination of flexion – eversion – extension – inversion.

Specific pawanmuktasana part 1 practices work on the ankle joint. This means that the respective muscles crossing the joint are rhythmically stimulated and de-stimulated. This alternate contraction and relaxation of the groups of muscles has a multi-layered effect on the system.

- These movements stimulate the subtle energies around the ankle joint and regulate its flow and movement.
- Blockages to the energy flow are removed and energy circulation in this region improves.
- Graded muscle contraction and relaxation removes the residual muscle tone that accumulates in a muscle due to mental stress and tension.
- Alternate stretching and contraction of the muscle squeezes out the accumulated toxins and sends them back into the blood (from where they travel to the liver for detoxification).
- Blood flow and lymph drainage in the region improve, increasing available nutrients and removing metabolic end products which lead to muscle fatigue.
- For the muscles to contract and relax alternately, the nerves need to fire in perfect synchronization. This means that the appropriate centres in the brain need to be firing in sync. Rhythmic and non-stressful stimulation of the central nervous system helps to reduce any excessive stimulation caused by the continual bombardment by stimuli from the five senses as well as from the mind.
- These movements trigger a balancing process in the autonomic nervous system (the sympathetic and para-sympathetic systems), thereby having a harmonizing effect.
- The pranic flow to that region improves due to the combination of movement and awareness.
- It has been postulated that specific emotions affect specific joints and over a period of time the cumulative effects cause damage there. These movements help prevent this type of effect.
- The kinaesthetic nerves supplying the joints are stimulated, rearranging the neuronal flow to the entire region.

PAWANMUKTASANA PART 1
(Anti-rheumatic group)

Prarambhik sthiti (base position)

The pawanmuktasana part 1 practices are performed while sitting in the base position with the legs outstretched, and the palms of the hands on the floor behind the buttocks. The whole body is relaxed, with the back, neck and head in a comfortable straight line.

1. For the joints of the toes, ankles, knees and hips:
Padanguli naman (toe bending)

This practice works on the toe joints. These joints are simple hinge joints with movement only possible in one axis, i.e. flexion and extension. The toes are consciously and voluntarily bent forward and backward, without moving the ankle, knee or hip joints. The muscles 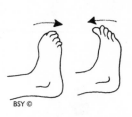 are relaxed and awareness should be maintained to keep the calf muscles and thigh muscles relaxed, so that the only movement is in the toes.

Goolf naman (ankle bending)

The ankle joints are hinge joints with some movement also possible in the lateral axis. Movements that take place in the ankle joints are: flexion –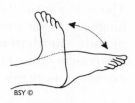

175

extension and inversion – eversion. This practice involves
flexion and extension of the ankle joint, i.e. bending the
ankle backwards and forwards.

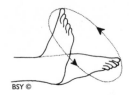

Goolf chakra (ankle rotation)
The ankle joint is also able to rotate.
This practice involves all possible movements across the ankle joint. The ankle
joint is rotated at a slow pace, thereby
involving flexion – extension as well as
inversion – eversion.

Goolf ghoornan (ankle crank)
This practice involves a passive
stretching movement at the ankle
joint. Folding the knee eliminates
usage of the thigh and calf muscles
and the passive rotation of the
ankle joint ensures maximum
movement of the joint.

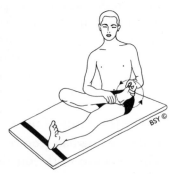

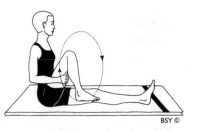

Janu naman (knee bending) and janu chakra (knee crank)
The next joint is the knee joint. The knee joint is a simple
hinge joint with a minor rotatory component. These asanas
include this latter, often neglected and hence weak,
component of the knee joint as well as its overused flexion –
extension mechanism.

Ardha titali (half butterfly), shroni chakra (hip rotation) and poorna titali (full butterfly)

The next three asanas deal with the hip joint, which is a complex ball and socket joint able to move in all three possible directions, i.e. flexion – extension, adduction – abduction and rotation. The hip joints connect the trunk with the legs. Given the upright posture of human beings, the weight of the entire body is literally transferred through this joint. This means the hip joints face great stresses even during routine activities. These asanas take the hip through its range of movement, including flexion and extension, abduction and adduction, and rotation.

177

2. For the joints of the fingers, hands, arms and shoulders:

We now move to the joints of the upper body. The main joints dealt with are the small joints in the hands and the major joints of the wrists, elbows and shoulders.

Mushtika bandhana (hand clenching)

This asana deals with the small joints of the hand, which are in the fingers. These joints are moved rhythmically and alternately. Movements across these joints are responsible for the fine and intricate movements of the fingers and the thumb, certain of which differentiate humans from animals. This region has an extremely bountiful nerve supply. Deep study of this quality has given rise to the science of reflexology, which postulates that appropriate sensory stimulation of the palm has the potential to heal and correct most imbalances in the body.

Manibandha naman (wrist bending) and manibandha chakra (wrist rotation)

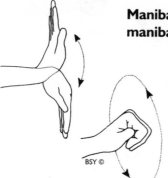

These practices work on the wrist joint. This is a complex joint in which the bones of the lower arm are connected to the hand via eight small bones known as carpal bones.

Kehuni naman (elbow bending)

The next joint is the elbow joint, which is a simple hinge joint with a limited range of movement.

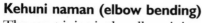
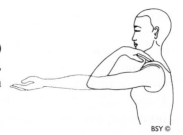

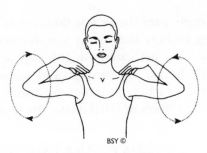

Skandha chakra (shoulder rotation)

The shoulder joint is a ball and socket joint, which is taken through its full range of movements by this asana.

3. For the neck:

Greeva sanchalana (neck movements)

The neck joint is one of the most sensitive and complex of the body's joints. It is located between the base of the skull and the vertebral column. Movements at the neck joint include flexion – extension, lateral flexion and rotation. The pawanmuktasana neck movements take the neck through this full range of movement, practice by practice.

This completes the first part of the pawanmuktasana series of asanas. This series deals with the major individual joints of the body. It helps release the toxins, emotions, residual stress and tensions that accumulate in and around these joints by use of regulated movements at each joint. At a subtler level, the movements release blockages in the pranic

179

pathways and regularize the pranic flow around these parts. It is interesting to note that many acupressure points and meridians are also activated by these practices. When combined with breath awareness and mental imaging techniques, these practices become much more potent and have far reaching effects in rebalancing the body's energies.

PAWANMUKTASANA PART 2
(Digestive/abdominal group)

Pawanmuktasana part 2 practices are particularly beneficial for strengthening the digestive system. Some also have a strong effect on the spine. The movements have a subtle yet deep impact on the muscles and joints of the vertebral column, and on the abdominal organs and the nervous system, due to the combined effect of changes in the blood and lymph supply, nerve supply, postural movements causing a change in direction of the gravitational force and various other factors.

These practices mainly affect the abdominal, pelvic and thoracic cavities and hence the digestive, genito-urinary, respiratory and cardiovascular systems. Specific asanas are: padotthanasana (raised legs pose), padachakrasana (leg rotation), pada sanchalanasana (cycling), supta pawanmukt-asana (leg lock pose), jhulana lurhakanasana (rocking and rolling), supta udarakarshanasana (sleeping abdominal stretch pose), shava udarakarshanasana (universal spinal twist) and naukasana (boat pose).

PAWANMUKTASANA PART 3
(Energy block postures)

Having worked on the basic systems of the body with the previous two sets of practices, we now move on to a group of asanas which works at a subtler level. The massaging effect of the pawanmuktasana part 3 asanas loosens and releases the obstructions that gradually accumulate in the body and pranic pathways due to long-term misuse of the whole system.

These practices clear the pranic pathways, resulting in a free flow of prana all over the body, effectively jump-starting the system and improving the vitality of the whole body. The neuroendocrine system is positively affected and the performance of almost all bodily systems is recalibrated and recharged.

The main practices are: rajju karshanasana (pulling the rope), gatyatmak meru vakrasana (dynamic spinal twist), chakki chalanasana (churning the mill), nauka sanchalanasana (rowing the boat), kashtha takshanasana (chopping wood), namaskarasana (salutation pose), vayu nishkasana (wind releasing pose), kauva chalasana (crow walking) and udarakarshanasana (abdominal stretch pose).

OTHER ASANAS

Tadasana (palm tree pose), tiryaka tadasana (swaying palm tree pose), kati chakrasana (wait rotating pose)
Tadasana helps improve physical and mental balance. The entire spine is stretched and loosened, which massages the area surrounding the nerves as they move between the vertebral column and the rest of the body. The abdominal muscles and internal abdominal and pelvic organs are stretched, and stale, stagnant blood is released into general circulation for purification.

The sideways-bending action of tiryaka tadasana massages and loosens the waist region and moves and strengthens the muscles alongside the spine. The twisting movement of kati chakrasana tones the waist, hips and back. The internal abdominal and pelvic organs are alternately squeezed and stretched by first twisting one way and then the other.

utthita lolasana

trikonasana

Utthita lolasana (swinging while standing pose), trikonasana (triangle pose)

These two asanas are performed from the standing posture. The main movement is at the waist. In utthita lolasana, the movement is in the forward and backward direction, while the movement in trikonasana is lateral. These movements tone the various postural muscles, helping restore normal and correct posture. At the same time, they help loosen and soften tensions in the waist and pelvic areas. These movements also have a balancing effect on mooladhara and swadhisthana chakras, which have a strong bearing on security and emotional and sexual desires.

182

majari-asana

vyaghrasana

bhujangasana

Marjari-asana (cat stretch pose), vyaghrasana (tiger pose), bhujangasana (cobra pose)

Today's lifestyle has a strongly disharmonizing effect on the body-mind and particularly on the vertebral column and other body structures responsible for maintaining appropriate body posture. Voluntary and deliberate turning of the vertebral column in the backward direction counteracts the excessive forward bending tendency of the vertebral column.

The alternate forward and backward bending of the whole entire back in marjari-asana, vyaghrasana and bhujangasana induces relaxation of the vertebral column and its associated structures, including muscles, nerves, blood and lymph vessels. Residual tensions, as well as knots of muscular tension, gradually subside, paving the way for the free flow of energy.

Vajrasana (thunderbolt pose), shashankasana (pose of the moon)

In vajrasana one sits with the buttocks resting on the cup formed by the ankles and feet, while the knees are folded. It is a beneficial way to sit during digestion.

183

Shashankasana is a simple yet effective asana which acts by balancing the sympathetic and parasympathetic flows in the body. It is a forward bending asana in which the palms and forehead are brought to the ground while sitting in vajrasana. The main chakras affected are swadhisthana and manipura.

Simhasana (lion pose), simhagarjanasana (roaring lion pose)
These asanas are performed using vajrasana as the base posture. Both prime and prepare the body for meditative processes by helping to introvert the mind, calm and streamline the mental processes and balance the brain wave patterns. Thought processes, mental agitation, runaway desires and other mental fluctuations come under the jurisdiction of anahata, vishuddhi and ajna chakras, which are affected by these asanas.

184

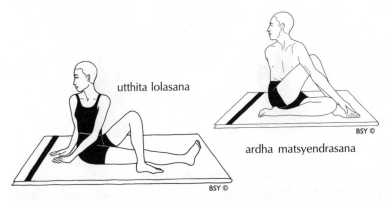

utthita lolasana

ardha matsyendrasana

Meru wakrasana (spinal twist), ardha matsyendrasana (half spinal twist)

Meru wakrasana is performed in the sitting posture and is a simplified version of ardha matsyendrasana. In both these asanas the spinal column is twisted to its maximum possible comfortable limit. In addition to the physical effect on the musculoskeletal system, this twisting of the spinal column creates a beneficial effect on the internal abdominal organs, especially the liver and spleen, thereby boosting their performance. It has a stimulatory effect on manipura chakra, thereby balancing the metabolic activities in the body. As manipura chakra is the generator of prana in the body, these practices boost pranic levels in the body.

Ardha matsyendrasana also affects ajna and vishuddhi chakras and hence has a stronger effect on regulating the flow of the pranas which have been awakened.

Dhyana veerasana (hero's meditation pose), gomukhasana (cow's face pose)

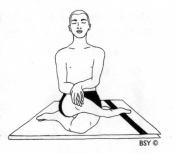

Dhyana veerasana can be considered a preparation for gomukhasana. Gomukhasana is a simple asana in which the hip muscles, arm muscles, thorax and abdomen are gently stretched. It utilizes muscles that are

185

not usually stretched and therefore tend to stiffen the body's posture. The physical stretching of these muscles has a direct correlation with the mental plane. This helps reduce anxiety levels and improves functioning of the abdominal organs, especially the kidneys. The kidneys are important in the removal of toxins from the body and also play an important role in managing the body's hormonal levels.

On the subtle dimension, gomukhasana has an impact on anahata and vishuddhi chakras, which deal with emotional perception, expression and communication. These aspects have been shown to have an important role in the genesis of the cancerous process. When functioning properly, anahata and vishuddhi chakras help in the management of emotional issues.

Surya namaskara (salutations to the sun)

Surya namaskara is a set of seven yogic postures dynamically woven into each other so that one flows from one asana into the next. A series of 24 postures makes one complete round. Surya namaskara has a profound effect on the entire system. The neuroendocrine system receives a thorough overhaul and recalibration. This practice also has a strong effect on awakening pranic energy and circulating it throughout the

body. On the psychic level it helps in regeneration of the pineal gland, which is supposed to be the master gland regulating the pituitary and hypothalamus. These control the endocrine system and a person's behavioural responses. Surya namaskara coupled with pranayama practices and mantra chanting have a pivotal role in raising pranic energy and purifying the chakras. This is a key process in helping the body to manage cancer and its toxic influence on the body. Surya namaskara can only be begun after the body and mind have been properly prepared using the earlier yogic practices.

Poorwa halasana (preliminary plough pose)

Poorwa halasana is an inverted asana performed while lying on the back. Both legs are raised, using the waist as a fulcrum, and moving them back as far as possible over the upper body. It prepares the body for the more important vipareeta karani asana.

paschimottanasana

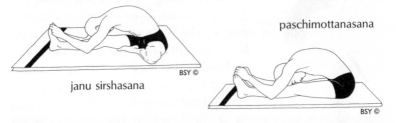

janu sirshasana

Janu sirshasana (head to knee pose), paschimottanasana (back stretching pose)

These forward bending asanas help release stiffness in the hip and pelvic regions. Sitting with the legs outstretched, one gradually leans forward, trying to grasp the toes with the fingers and touch the nose to the knees without bending them.

It has been postulated that stiffness in the pelvic region is associated with unresolved issues regarding manipura,

187

swadhisthana and mooladhara chakras. These asanas help to stretch and loosen this region and bring hidden, unresolved issues to the fore in a gentle manner.

Eka pada pranamasana (one-legged prayer pose)

This is one of the simplest of the balancing asanas, yet it can be difficult to master. Starting in the standing position, one leg is folded at the knee and the foot is placed on the opposite thigh. The important point and also the most difficult one is to maintain complete balance in this posture for a short period of time. Difficulty in maintaining the pose reflects the fluctuations of the mind. Gradually, one-pointedness is achieved with practice, a fact reflected in the steadiness of the posture.

Ushtrasana (camel pose), supta vajrasana (sleeping thunderbolt pose)

These two backward bending asanas start in the base position of vajrasana. In ushtrasana one rises on the knees and bends backwards, trying to grasp the ankles. In supta vajrasana, one bends backwards from the waist and tries to rest the crown of the head on the ground, while pressing upward through the chest. Both these practices are a good antidote for the continued forward bending and stooping postures we use all day while carrying out various mundane tasks, including computer and other desk work, physical labour and household chores.

Vishuddhi, manipura and swadhisthana chakras are the main centres stimulated by these practices. Consequently, issues regarding communication, expression, energy distribution or dissipation, metabolism, digestion, insecurities and phobias can start to be resolved with these asanas.

Vipareeta karani asana (inverted pose)

This inverted asana is a perfect counterpose for the effect of gravity on the body due to the upright posture of human beings. The legs and hips are raised in the air and supported with a stable stand created by cupping the hands under the hips, with the elbows and shoulders pressed into the floor. The feet, knees and waist are in a straight line, while the torso is at a 45 degree angle to the floor. The body is held in a relaxed manner. This asana has many benefits, including the circulatory system, the internal organs and the neuroendocrine and respiratory systems. At a subtler level it activates vishuddhi and manipura chakras. It is also the basis for vipareeta karani mudra, which activates the whole pranic system, especially the chakras.

Dhanurasana (bow pose), shalabh-asana (locust pose)

These two backward bending asanas are performed while lying on the front. In dhanurasana, the body is brought into the shape of a bow, with the hands clutching the ankles so that the arms form the string of the bow. In shalabh-asana, only the legs and feet are raised off the ground, this time without any support from

189

the hands. The onus of maintaining this posture falls on the back muscles and to a lesser extent, the thigh muscles. This not only strengthens the back and thigh musculature, but also acts on the internal abdominal organs, spinal cord and urogenital organs. Swadhisthana and manipura chakras are strongly activated using these asanas.

Siddhasana (accomplished pose for men) and siddha yoni asana (accomplished pose for women)

This meditative posture is very important, especially in the context of managing cancer. In addition to the physical disturbances created by cancer, the mind and emotions are also thrown out of balance and start fluctuating wildly. The mind is a very powerful force and often the thoughts it generates are so strong that they can alter the physical manifestation of events. This asana helps us to channel the mind and emotions.

In this posture, one of the heels presses into the perineum and the other into the pubis. This exerts powerful pressure on mooladhara and swadhisthana chakras, which are associated with emotions, insecurities and phobias, and tend to pull and push the mind in their specific directions. Applying moola bandha and vajroli mudra (for men) or sahajoli mudra (for women) helps calm the mind and imparts focus, direction and purpose.

190

PRANAYAMA

Yogic breathing

The process of breathing has three components – abdominal, thoracic and clavicular. The lungs are enclosed in a closed bony cavity called the thoracic cage and respiration occurs due to differences in the air pressure inside the lungs and outside in the atmosphere. Reduction in the air pressure inside the lungs causes air to move into the lungs via the nose, trachea and bronchi and vice versa for exhalation. The movements of the thoracic cage, which surrounds the lungs, control the pressure in the lungs.

The groups of muscles attached to the thoracic cage control its movements. The thoracic cage is made up of the vertebral column behind and the sternum in front, joined by the 12 pairs of ribs on both sides.

Conscious, rhythmic and coordinated movements of the thoracic cage lead to a complete range of movement of this area during breathing. Inhalation is initiated by the downward movement of the diaphragm (associated with the outward movement of the abdominal wall), followed in proper coordination with expansion of the thoracic region and terminated by the upward movement of the clavicles. Exhalation follows the exact reverse pattern - release of air from the clavicles followed by the chest and lastly the abdomen. However, it is essential to learn to listen to the body while performing these actions, as the movements do not occur in isolation but together as a complete unit.

The benefits of this breathing activity are too numerous to mention here. It would be more practical and much simpler for the reader to pause and try this way of breathing in order to experience the changes.

Bhramari pranayama (humming bee breath)

Bhramari is yet another example of simplicity coupled with matchless effectiveness. The brain is enclosed in the bony cranial cavity and rests on the neck as its base. Setting up

soothing vibrations in the brain matrix is a good way to relax the brain and improve circulation to it. Bhramari achieves just that by setting up vibrations in the brain through a humming sound from the voice box. This is amplified by closing the ears with the fingers, so as to cut off the external incoming sound vibrations and to amplify the internal humming. Bhramari relieves stress and increases the healing capacity of the body.

Nadi shodhana 1–4 (alternate nostril breathing)

Nadi shodhana is a modification of the breathing pattern so that one breathes consciously while alternating the breath from one nostril to the other. The flow of the breath is manipulated by opening and closing the nostrils, using gentle pressure from the ring finger and thumb on the left and right nostrils respectively. Keeping the breath relaxed and normal, one starts by rotating through the cycle of inhalation and exhalation in alternate nostrils. Gradually the duration of inhalation and exhalation is increased over a period of time. After reaching a comfort zone with each stage, one moves onto the next stage, gradually advancing without any strain or tension. As the stages progress, the ratios of inhalation and exhalation are controlled, then internal breath retention is introduced, followed by external breath retention.

Nadi shodhana pranayama is a simple yet very powerful practice. It can be practised anywhere while maintaining the necessary precautions. It clears the pathways for the flow of the pranas or subtle forces.

Ujjayi pranayama (the psychic breath)

Ujjayi pranayama is categorized as a tranquillizing pranayama, which means it induces a peaceful, calm state by activating the parasympathetic nervous system (relaxation response). It is one of the most important of the therapeutic yogic breathing techniques and is widely used during meditation. Ujjayi is very simple to practise. The glottis is lightly contracted so that a gentle, whispering sound comes from the throat during both inhalation and exhalation. An effort is made to lengthen the breath and to make it as smooth and even as possible. The whole body should be relaxed during the practice.

Kapalbhati pranayama (frontal brain cleansing breath)

Kapalbhati is a pranayama from the shatkarma group of cleansing practices, used to cleanse the frontal brain. To practise kapalbhati, exhale with a forceful contraction of the abdominal muscles and then let inhalation occur without effort as a passive recoil. This reverses the usual pattern in which the in breath is active and the out breath is passive. The necessary precautions for cancer patients should be strictly observed.

4: Introduction to Yoga and Cancer Research

34

Yoga and Cancer Research: A Comparative Analysis Sample

Research is that aspect of science which deals with the scientific analysis of information so that we can better understand the subject. Research can be defined as a process of establishing objectively quantifiable and verifiable data to logically explain the mechanism of action of a specific phenomenon, the results of which can be and have been repeated elsewhere also by objective and non-biased people under similar conditions. The ability to repeat results is subject to the set parameters being observed and the experimental environment being recreated as defined by the original experimenters.

Scientists of the hoary past conducted experiments and made detailed and minute observations about various phenomena, external as well as internal. Based on these observations, they made inferences and tested their authenticity back on the phenomenon itself. They then drew conclusions and devised theories regarding life and the role of human beings in the entire scheme of existence and their links with the whole cosmos. This led them to many wonderful discoveries about nature and her ways. Their laboratory was the mind and their analysis was based on personal experience. Distillation of these observations over generations led them to discover the natural laws which govern the macro- and microcosmic universe.

Modern scientists use slightly different methods to come to a similar end point. Based on empirical observations, they postulate theories which are tested on the basis of rigorous logical analysis and followed up, where necessary and appropriate, with experiments on animals and then on humans. Both aim to achieve a greater understanding of the natural phenomena governing health and illness (in this instance), so as to rectify illness and impart positive health to one and all.

This chapter endeavours to arouse your curiosity and share the work put into both these subjects by others. Curiosity and a desire to know or understand the functioning and behaviour of natural phenomena are at the heart of research. The breakthrough occurs only when the concept is grasped and internalized, and then there is a paradigm shift in understanding of the situation and a quantum leap occurs, allowing the solution to appear before us. It was this leap in consciousness that Newton experienced when he saw the apple falling, and the entire theory of gravity unfolded before him. The same applies to Einstein and his theory of relativity, Edward Jenner and his concept of vaccination, and many others.

This chapter is a modest attempt to bring together various pieces of the jigsaw, so that we may have a wider perspective on cancer. By comparing the two methodologies and grasping the parallels between ancient yogic principles and modern medical therapeutical research, a greater understanding can be generated so that we may tackle the problem of cancer more efficiently. To do so, let us briefly consider how the two methodologies approach the causation of cancer (including diet, stress and emotions), and its management.

Causation of cancer
Yoga maintains that while disease, in this case cancer, manifests in the body, it originates elsewhere. The roots of cancer can be found in the subtler dimensions of our existence, viz. in manomaya kosha, the mental-emotional dimension, in pranamaya kosha, the bioplasmic energy dimension, and in the causal dimensions. The yogic approach says that the basic problem lies in defective and distorted pranic flow to

the specific area over a long period of time. This manifests in the body as a cancerous tumour. Reinforcement of this defect causes changes in annamaya kosha (biochemical and DNA changes in the cell), which result in breaching the multiple autoprotective and corrective systems of the body, resulting in the growth and spread of the tumour.

Pranic distortion can take place due to factors in the physical dimension, the mental-emotional dimension or from the causal dimensions. Yoga holds the view that thoughts, especially with a strong emotional content, can become potent forces which can modify the pranic flow. This is one of the important factors in cancer formation today. Each dimension has multiple protective mechanisms to try to limit or nullify such 'negative' patterns, which need to be breached before the disease progresses further. Multiple such errors in more than one kosha remaining uncorrected for a long period of time accumulate and converge in the annamaya kosha or manifest physical dimension. Here they damage the most susceptible link in the chain, which leads to cancer.

Modern research has revealed that cancer is undoubtedly a genetic disorder, in the sense that cancer is caused due to genetic changes, which alter the basic behaviour of cells. It has now been proven beyond doubt that cancer is caused by multi-step, non-lethal genetic mutations. The modern medical viewpoint holds that there are multiple key risk factors implicated in the causation of cancer. These differ with the type of cancer.

However, scientists have discovered that there are some common pathways in a majority of cancers, irrespective of causative factors, including dietary factors, chemical carcinogens, environmental factors, stress, and so on. More than half of all the cancers studied have revealed mutations in a specific tumour suppressor gene known as the p53 gene. This gene has many anti-cancer mechanisms, and plays a role in apoptosis, genetic stability, and inhibition of angiogenesis. Mutations in the p53 gene occur due to various factors which include DNA damage due to exposure to various types of radiation, chemical agents, stress, osmotic disturbances, and acid-base imbalances, to name a few important factors (Vakhrusheya, 2008).[6] This agrees with the yogic viewpoint that factors from different koshas, e.g. mental stress from manomaya kosha, radiation from annamaya kosha and pranamaya kosha, etc., converge and manifest in the physical dimension as a cancerous process.

Yoga also maintains that prana, bioplasmic energy, plays a central role in the progress of cancer or in its regression and healing. More recent research has shown that injury to the mitochondria, the energy generator of the cell, is also implicated in many cancerous processes (Wallace, 2005).[7] The mitochondria is also the centre of cellular respiration. Damage to the mitochondria affects the mechanism of cellular respiration, which releases harmful chemicals that can lead to mitochondrial mutations. Some studies have shown that mitochondrial dysfunction appears to play a role in the causation of cancer (Brandon & Wallace, 2006).[8]

Cancer and dietetics

The yogic viewpoint looks at diet in two broad dimensions – the physical diet from which the bodily structures have originated, and a subtler diet which nourishes the mind, emotions, pranas and causal dimensions. Both provide pranic energy to the body, which is essential for maintaining a healthy mind, emotions and psyche. The yogic scriptures place great importance on food, its nutritional capacity and its role in positive health. They also specify that this food is also the carrier of the subtle pranas and hence can have a deep-seated impact on human health.

According to yoga, food can be classified into three categories, depending upon its quality – sattwic, rajasic or tamasic. Pure, sattwic food increases the life force or energy, promotes health and imparts joy and cheerfulness to the person eating it. Such food tastes good, is moist and stable in nature and very good for health. Rajasic food usually has a bitter, pungent or sour taste, and is drying. It is stimulating in nature and an excess can be harmful to the body. Tamasic food is stale, tasteless, impure, and putrid/fermented. It has a negative impact on the body, creating disease, inertia, drowsiness and negativity in the person eating it, and can be considered as an instigator of ill health. Yoga thus advises us to have a judicious mixture of sattwic and rajasic foods in normal times. In disease conditions, only sattwic food is prescribed as it can help to reverse the excess of tamas and rajas in the body.

Studies in the field of nutrition have shown that diet plays an important role in cancer. All foods have been shown to be potential BRMs or behaviour response modifiers. Foods can affect the DNA either through direct contact or due to the chemical reactions they set up by their presence in the body (Simone, 2000).[9] Many studies have conclusively proven the carcinogenic effect of certain foods like processed meats, and of food preparation methods such as barbecuing and pickling. There have also been studies linking a lower risk of cancer with certain foods rich in phytochemicals and antioxidants, such as fresh fruits and vegetables.

While it is excepted that a nutritious diet is essential to maintain the body and help face the stress which the disease process of cancer and its treatment inflicts on the body, attention is now also being given to the type of diet. A fresh, organic diet free from meat products is increasingly considered more beneficial as it includes more phytochemicals and other protective ingredients. This in turn imparts more ability to a person to fight cancer. Similarly, food items such as saturated fatty acids and some meat products, which are now known to have harmful effects on the system by predisposing cells towards cancerous degeneration, should be avoided (Quillin, 2000).[10]

It is being realized that the food we eat can play a strong role in inhibiting or accelerating the cancerous process. Experiments by A. B. Robinson et al (1994) explored the relationship between diet and cancer, and found that diets with the least optimum balance of nutrients had the greatest inhibitory effect on the growth of cancer. The rate of onset

201

and severity of tumours was caused to vary over a 20-fold range by means of dietary balance alone. These experiments suggest that dietary variation in general and intentional malnutrition in particular should be given special attention in the control of existing cancers in humans (Robinson, 1994).[11]

Stress

According to yoga, stress is experienced when a person is exposed to a situation which demands specific results requiring active effort. Stress thus causes wear and tear on the entire system at all levels, including body, mind and consciousness. If our recuperative powers are able to regenerate the loss created and improve on earlier capacities, then such stress, now termed 'eustress', can be beneficial. However, if the stress places such demands on the system that damage and hence impairment result, then such stress is known as 'distress', which is harmful in the short as well as long term. This stress can originate in the body, mind, intellect, emotions or psyche. Depending upon the nature of the stress, it can lead to imbalances in the koshas and culminate in a cancerous process manifesting on the physical level. Yoga aims to increase our recuperative capacities, thereby increasing the threshold of conversion of eustress to distress. Various yogic practices help in preventing and managing cancer effectively.

Modern medical studies have proven that stress has a strong impact on the genes, genetic behaviour and also on the mutations taking place in the genes. Studies have shown that chronic stress has a negative impact on health and on the neuroimmune apparatus in general. Newer research is underway to isolate the direct links between stress and cancer. Such studies have shown a great deal of promise, but need more verification before firm conclusions can be drawn.

No research is needed to bring home the fact that stress is a part of our lives. How we handle that stress has an impact on our health. Every day, we hear more and more about the harm it may cause to our minds and bodies, from anxiety attacks to heart disease. Evidence is accumulating that there is some link between stress and developing certain kinds of cancer, as well as how the disease progresses.

Multiple studies have measured the impact of stress on our immune systems and ability to fight disease. At Ohio State University, researcher Dr Ron Glaser, PhD, found that students under pressure had slower healing wounds and took longer to produce immune system cells that kill invading organisms. Dr Barry Spiegel MD, a leader in the field of psychosomatic medicine, found that metastatic breast cancer patients lived longer when they participated in support groups. Other studies have gone so far as to show that women who experienced traumatic life events or losses in previous years had significantly higher rates of breast cancer.

Every day our bodies are exposed to cancer-causing agents in the air, food and water. Typically, our immune system recognizes those abnormal cells and kills them before they produce a tumour. There are three important things that can happen to prevent cancer from developing – the immune system can prevent the agents from invading in the first place, the DNA can repair the abnormal cells, or killer T-cells can kill off cancer cells. According to Dr Lorenzo Cohen, PhD, research has shown that stress can lower the body's ability to do each of those things. However, he cautions against jumping to conclusions that stress alone is the causative factor for cancer. Part of the reason stress may be linked to cancer, he says, is simply that when people are under pressure they make poor choices – they begin smoking, stop exercising, start eating unhealthy foods – factors that are also linked to cancer. The advice of Reina Marino, MD, a physician and consultant for the American Cancer Society, includes practices like deep breathing, meditation, imagery and mindfulness to combat cancer more effectively.

Cancer and emotions

A diagnosis of cancer shatters the emotions and the entire being descends into a state of turmoil. Emotions like shock, anger, sorrow, denial and other related feelings surface, turning our lives upside down. While there is some dispute about suppressed or unexpressed emotions causing cancer, there can be no doubt that the presence of a negative emotional state is certainly not helpful in the effort to combat cancer. Many studies have shown the ability of yogic practices to improve the quality of life, provide emotional stability and induce a state of positive thinking, which not only helps to boost the immune system, but also induces a sense of wellbeing. All these factors have a role to play in the overall health status and the ability of the body to fight illness. Studies on emotional management, mindfulness and yoga have shown that adopting yoga in one's daily lifestyle helps practitioners to rein in the runaway train of emotions and embrace a more positive outlook towards illness, which allows the disease process to be managed in a more objective and focused manner.

Emotions seem to play a crucial role in the genesis and healing of serious disease such as cancer (and literally, laughter seems to be a type of medicine). For instance, any kind of unexpected shock (including a cancer diagnosis) can have a devastating effect on health and/or the immune system until it is resolved and healed in any number of ways. A similar mechanism seems to apply when a person lives in fear. Therefore, one of the first tasks in a successful healing journey may be working at re-establishing the greatest possible measure of inner peace and confidence. Dr Jurgen Buche observes that motivation to overcome cancer and live wholly again can play a pivotal role in cancer patients rallying themselves against the disease, and this driving force can be crucial in reviving the failing defences of the patient.

Unhealed emotional wounds, traumas and repressed memories have a powerful effect on us and a lot of energy is expended in trying to control the damage they cause. Releasing such traumas releases a lot of energy, which can be utilized more constructively, especially when one is affected by an illness like cancer. In her groundbreaking book, *The Molecules of Emotion*, Dr Candace Pert discusses at length and in great scientific detail how emotions have a tangible basis and also a very strong effect on health. Unhealed and unexpressed emotions are like ticking atom bombs in the body with the potential to trigger off large scale cascading effects, leading to crippling diseases like cancer. The simplest way to manage them is knowing how to channel emotional energy and learning a system that provides a constructive outlet for such feelings.

Research on yoga, health and cancer

Studies are underway to try and pinpoint the direct effect of yoga therapy on cancer management. The prospects for obtaining a direct correlation between yoga and reversal of the cancer process are promising. In addition, it has been shown that yogic practices have a positive effect on controlling and reducing the side effects of chemotherapy, radiotherapy and surgery. Yoga also improves the patient's quality of life – a very important point for the person with cancer. Other relevant research findings point out that yogic practices bring about positive changes in the personality, thereby improving general health.

Yoga and health

Studies have shown that yogic practices have strong healing properties which have been used to heal degenerative diseases like asthma, heart disease, arthritis, and so on.[12] Amongst other mechanisms of action, yogic practices have been shown to manipulate the prana or subtle force present in the body, causing a general improvement in the functioning of the entire body-mind complex. Yogic practices such as asana, pranayama and meditative techniques have a beneficial effect not only in illness, but also in improving the functioning of the organs and systems in the body, including the psycho-neuroimmune system, metabolic system, neuroendocrine system and so on.

In conclusion

This chapter is not intended to be an exhaustive synopsis of the medical research being undertaken on cancer, yoga and health. Such an attempt is beyond the scope of this book. However, it attempts to bring to our notice the striking parallels between the results of various medical and other health research and yogic principles as assimilated from the painstaking research of the ancient yogis. This comparative analysis provides us with clues to channel our own inquisitiveness into conducting enquiries so that we can achieve a convincing and effective solution. However, we need to bear in mind that the proof of the pudding lies in its eating, not just in observing and enquiring alone!

It is hoped that this chapter is able to awaken a spirit of enquiry and a non-dogmatic and constructive approach towards cancer specifically and towards life in general. Instead of limiting ourselves to evidence-based medical practice, we can move into the more open, challenging and rewarding practice-based evidence. Do not accept things only at face value. Try them out for yourself. Use your own common sense and intelligence. Conduct your own research. Your body and mind are your laboratory, yoga is the research and positive and wholesome health is the final outcome.

Yoga represents the search of humankind for a higher reality not visible to the naked eye. Research is nothing but a refinement of the original search. The facts and opinions about yoga as a means of cancer management presented in this book will be enriched by your own experiences. The search to heal cancer and the search of a kundalini seeker might seem diametrically opposed to each other, yet both begin with and work in the same domain of body-mind and spirit. As such, the means used by those sublime seekers will help your search as well.

After all, how many of us have actually seen an electron and understood it in all its dimensions? Yet we do not hesitate to turn on the switch to use an electric light bulb or any other electric appliance. Our needs and the needs of the scientist delving into the sublime details of quantum mechanics have very little in common. Yet the same electron supplies the needs of both. In the same manner, yoga provides us with a means of carrying out experiments in the laboratory of the body-mind-spirit. It provides us with knowledge of how to use the laboratory apparatus. What we want to achieve from these experiments is entirely up to us alone. Be it health management, happiness, fitness, positive health, a way of life, material success, power or even nirvana or samadhi, yoga provides us with the means to achieve these results in our own laboratory. This has been the experience of a multitude of yogis down the ages. We invite you to test it out in your own laboratory.

Appendicies

Some Useful Mantras

A mantra can be chanted in two ways, either as a specific sadhana practice or continually as a *sumiran* or constant remembrance. When chanted as a sadhana, a few guidelines need to be observed for greater efficacy. When practised as a constant remembrance, there are no restrictions for the chanting. Chanting of a mantra can be done loudly, in a muted voice or whispered, or mentally according to individual inclination.

When chanted as a sadhana, the following guidelines are beneficial.

- Decide upon a fixed number of repetitions and stick to the number for the duration decided upon.
- Set aside a specific place where you can practise your mantra. Let it be your own space, and not involved with your other commitments.
- Fix a time during the day or night to practise the mantra and try to maintain it.
- Try and complete the number of repetitions you initially decided upon.
- You can include a spiritual symbol or a candle flame to fix your attention on while practising the mantra. (This does not have any bearing on your religious background, although you can choose a symbol from your religious background too if you feel comfortable with it.)
- You can combine the mantra practice with the corresponding yantra for greater efficacy.

- It is best to receive the mantra from a guru who can guide you on the path

The following is a list of some mantras which can be useful for nada yoga practices and also for relieving distress and agony in general.

1. *Mahamrityunjaya mantra* is a healing mantra dedicated to Lord Mahamrityunjaya, the conqueror of death.

   Om trayambakam yajaamahe sugandhim pushtivardhanam.
   Urvaarukamiva bandhanaat mrityormuksheeya maamritaat.

   ॐ त्र्यम्बकं यजामहे सुगन्धिं पुष्टिवर्धनम् ।
   उर्वारुकमिव बन्धनात् मृत्योर्मुक्षीय मामृतात् ॥

2. *Om namah Shivaaya* (ॐ नम: शिवाय) is a rejuvenating mantra dedicated to Lord Shiva, the god of transformation.

3. *Om namo Naaraayanaaya* (ॐ नमो नारायणाय) is the mantra of Narayana, the cosmic source of all creatures.

4. *Om dum Durgaayai namah* (ॐ दुं दुर्गायै नम:). Durga, the benevolent form of Devi or Shakti, is a protective goddess and her mantra has a protective effect.

5. *Om gam Ganapataye namah* (ॐ गं गणपतये नम:) is the mantra of Ganesha, the deity presiding over good fortune, and the dispeller of all obstacles.

6. *Bija mantras*: are seed forms of the mantras. They do not have any linguistic meaning. However, these mantras resonate with the deeper layers of consciousness and produce effects there. A useful bija mantra is *Aim hreem kleem Om* (ऐं ह्रीं क्लीं ॐ), the mantra given by Swami Satyananda for Rikhiapeeth. It is the bija mantra for Devi, personifying the three forms of Kali, Durga and Lakshmi – to destroy evil and negative tendencies, to form positive and constructive tendencies, and to bestow an abundance of health, money and prosperity.

7. *Chakra bijas* are the seed sounds corresponding to each chakra.
   - Mooladhara   *lam*   लं
   - Swadhisthana   *vam*   वं

- Manipura   *ram*   रं
- Anahata   *yam*   यं
- Vishuddhi   *ham*   हं
- Ajna   *aum*   ॐ

8. *Om aim hreem kleem chaamundaayai vichche* (ॐ ऐं ह्रीं क्लीं चामुण्डायै विच्चे) is the mantra of Devi. It bestows good health, wisdom and peace on the practitioner.

9. *Gayatri mantra* is one of the most commonly used and powerful mantras. It raises the pranic level in the body, imparts vitality and removes diseases and obstacles

> *Om bhoorbhuvah svaha tatsaviturvarenyam bhargo devasya dheemahi dhiyo yo nah prachodayaat.*

> ॐ भूर्भुव: स्व: तत्सवितुर्वरेण्यं।
> भर्गो देवस्य धीमहि धियो यो न: प्रचोदयात्॥

Some Common Yantras

Mahamrityunjaya yantra

Mahamrityunjaya is a form of Lord Shiva. Traditionally, Shiva is known as the lord of destruction. This interpretation needs to be understood properly if one is grasp the complete significance of this deity. Shiva is said to destroy the evil and negative tendencies within us. In this light Shiva can better be termed as the lord of transformation – destroying negative tendencies and replacing them with positive ones. In the form of Mahamrityunjaya, Shiva is said to be the conqueror of death. This yantra is most beneficial in all illnesses. Meditation and use of this yantra is said to impart good health and longevity to the practitioner.

Ganesha yantra

Ganesha is the famous elephant-headed son of Shiva and Parvati. He is also known as *Vighnaharta* or the destroyer of all calamities and the bestower of happiness. Regular use of the Ganesha yantra is said to impart these qualities to the practitioner.

214

Sri yantra

This is one of the most powerful yantras in tantra. It is supposed to symbolize Devi – Prakriti. The entire cosmos comes under the jurisdiction of Prakriti. As such, we and our afflictions and ailments come under her sway too. Regular use of the Sri yantra helps to fulfil all our desires.

Gayatri yantra

Gayatri is the mantra of the pranas. She also has a very deep link with the Sun, the cosmic giver of prana for the earth. This yantra is said to have a beneficial effect on the individual pranas residing within us.

Shiva yantra

The Shiva yantra is the yantric symbolization of Shiva, cosmic consciousness. Using this yantra is said to remove obstacles and ignorance and bestow happiness and joy on the practitioner

215

Chakra yantras

Regular practice of the yantras corresponding to each chakra results in a gradual and graded activation of these chakras. This results in a better pranic flow and removes the pranic blockages and distortions which have accumulated over a period of time.

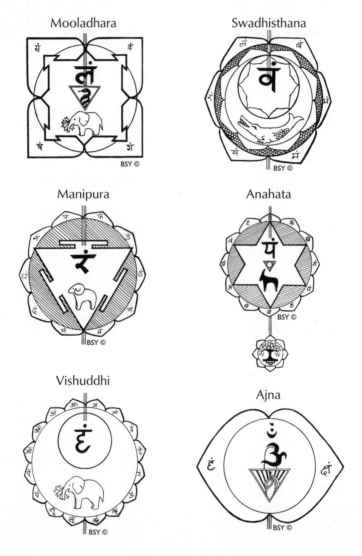

Mooladhara

Swadhisthana

Manipura

Anahata

Vishuddhi

Ajna

Can One Prevent Cancer?

Marguerite Bugler

This is a personal account by Miss Marguerite Bugler, written in 1969, of her experiences overcoming cancer. She was struck by cancer in 1950 and given a very poor prognosis. It did not help that in those days few effective therapies for cancer treatment existed. This more or less forced her to explore different avenues in trying to save herself. Hers is a voyage of discovery and the discerning reader will be able to note the parallels she speaks of with yogic principles and newer discoveries of occurrences of cancer. She affirms the strong impact of yoga on her life and health. She suffered intense fears and doubts, but through divine inspiration, yoga and a special diet, she was able to defeat the disease. Though much of the factual background and scientific understanding may have changed since 1969, the underlying message and inspiration remains the same.

Introduction

The information contained in these pages is based upon my personal experiences and observations. It comes equally from well known sources in the domain of natural therapeutics. I pay homage to all the learned people whose work and research has shed some light upon the real causes of cancer and the means of protecting oneself from this terrible complaint. I express my very deep gratitude to them, and also to Professor Raymond Lautie, Doctor of Science, who for forty years has studied the problem of cancer and allowed me to borrow much information from his remarkable writings.

Cancer in any form does not come all of a sudden. It is not an accidental illness, but the manifestation of a degenerative condition which is increased from one generation to another. It begins at birth with a life not shaped to the laws of nature. However, it is not necessarily fatal. We have the means of preventing it and even curing it, if none of the vital organs are totally destroyed and if the patient still has sufficient vitality to react.

On the strength of this assertion, I beg to expose the conclusive causes of my cancerous condition, and also the method applied leading me to a complete cure. By the grace of God, Monsieur Pierre Bocquillon has been permitted to save numerous sufferers and to cure me. This is a debt that cannot be repaid in a whole lifetime.

About the author

I was born on December 26, 1900, in Tunisia, very tiny but 'well made with a strong heart' according to the naval doctor who assisted my mother at my birth. My dear mother was unable to feed me herself, her milk having no nutritional value. That was the reason for my parents' return to France.

1901–1904 was spent in Belfort, France. A very kind but nervous aunt undertook the feeding of this baby brought from Africa. I lived there until the age of four, struggling against the bitter cold, snow, ice and the usual children's illnesses: measles and whooping cough. Two brothers arrived, increasing the family. My parents decided to settle in Paris. Very poor, they could only find a small house, two little rooms with no sunshine.

Paris – childhood: Shut in at school all day long, and evenings spent at home, we needed both air and space. Only Sunday outings in the fine season permitted our escape into the woods around Paris. What a joy, at last, to be able to run about in the green! Nevertheless, this was insufficient, and anaemia set in, in spite of plenty of good and varied food. A violent attack of scarlet fever at the age of ten increased my bad health, provoking definite harm to both sight and hearing. Then frequent nose-bleeding and a worse state of anaemia appeared, in spite of tonics and the raw meat advised, which I ate with disgust.

1914–1918: Then came the First World War. My father was mobilized, and had four years of terrible suffering and restrictions, marking him for the rest of his life. I was able to continue my studies, thanks to my parents' sacrifices. But fatigue and privation aggravated my mother's cardiac condition. My father returned, ill and worn out by these four years of war. We had all suffered from lack of food, but even more so from the absence of coal.

1918–1919: Having obtained my diploma as a school teacher, I taught in the schools of Paris from the age of eighteen. My mother was very ill and had more and more frequent stays in hospital. She passed away in 1926 after a terrible heart attack. My grief was dreadful.

1926–1939: I remained alone with my father and two brothers. My days were exhausting in overcrowded class-rooms, with 60, 70 and 80 pupils, and I had to travel long distances to and from the schools. I had heavy work at home for the upkeep of linen and clothes for my family. My dear father helped me very much.

At the age of thirty-two, I began to suffer from trachitis-bronchitis, increasing more seriously each winter, from sore throats, influenza and facial neuralgia. My brothers left home to marry. Life was more peaceful and calm. But in spite of that, my health altered more and more. Intense fatigue was caused by my profession. I suffered from sleeplessness, which nothing would overcome. The doctor sent me to the country each year for a complete rest, various medicines having had no effect.

1939–1943: A new war began, longer and more atrocious. Neither fire nor food were available. The famine was terrible. My father could no longer bear the fatigue of long hours queuing to obtain a half a cauliflower, nor the moral suffering caused by the German occupation. He was carried away by peritonitis on May 1st, 1943. This new shock was so terrible that my state of health became even worse. I became thinner and thinner (39 kilograms when dressed). After an X-ray (radiographic) the school doctor gave me less than eight days to live if I remained in Paris.

1943 – Megena, Upper Savoy, French Alps: Thanks to a friend, well placed in the Ministry of National Education, I was able to leave for Megena, rejoining the children evacuated from Paris. There I found pure air, but harmful and insufficient food (turnips for animals). I gave the mountain children lessons in return for a little milk, which did me no good, as it lacked vitamins. This food, unsuitable for human needs, provoked a serious attack of enteritis which nothing could stop. A friend remaining in Paris sent me some gastric dressing to relieve the pain.

1944: Having heard of the return of a great surgeon, Andre Picaud, at the Sallanches hospital, I decided to consult him. After a very thorough X-raying, the doctor advised me to come to Paris as quickly as possible, and see a well known specialist in digestive organs, as my caecum and colon were in a very bad condition.

1945: Returning to Paris, I saw the specialist and had new X-rays. The treatment ordered made me ill. The injections provoked fainting and diarrhoea, the meat advised made me sick, and so I gave up this doctor, his treatment and the animal food.

1946–1950: In this period my food was chiefly composed of milk, butter, cheese, vegetables cooked in water, sometimes an egg, fruit, a little white bread, rice and semolina. I put on weight without, however, regaining my vitality. In 1950, a tiny lump appeared on my left breast and did not disappear, so this time I consulted a naturopathic doctor, who advised me to drink seawater and gave me injections of '816'. Shortly after, I learned that these injections were against cancer, but had not so far cured anybody. My condition became worse, with loss of vitality, low blood pressure, uterine haemorrhaging, frequent fainting, total insomnia and trachitis-bronchitis; I coughed without ceasing night and day. Another doctor diagnosed the condition as 'cancer of the uterus'. The National Education doctor gave me 'long leave'.

1952: A friend put me in contact with a great radiologist, a very pious and pure man, who had already cured hundreds of patients often given up on by their doctor. The result of his examination taken from a lock of my hair showed cancerous tendencies as follows: aorta 25%, renal glands 35%, colon 35%, caecum 40%, uterus 45%, mammary glands 60%, fibroid 10%. There were serious deficiencies in calcium, magnesium, fluorine, silica, phosphorus, etc.

This extraordinary man, who had cured himself of his disease thanks to his radiology clock (hypertension, urea, cancer) advised me to take the following diet. Pap or soup made from whole flour in the morning and in the evening (corn and wheat to be freshly ground); raw ripe fruits between meals; at midday raw fruits or raw vegetables, or green salad with lemon and oil (never vinegar), steamed vegetables, and a diet drink made from medicinal plants (anthylline, which included strawberry roots, fennel, hyssop, plantain, sweet smelling vervain, marjoram, sandal, horsetail, liquorice, marshmallow, angelica, coriander, nettles, chervil, thistles, ash, mint, etc.).

Revived by the sunshine and high altitude, helped by complete rest and the therapeutic treatment of Louis Kuhne (author of *The New Science of Curing, Based on the Unity of all Illnesses*), my vitality returned so quickly that I was bound toward a cure, and the radiologist himself was amazed.

When school reopened, my unexpected resurrection had an extraordinary effect upon all, as they had thought they would never see me again.

– But you appear cured!
– I think I am.
– No more pains?
– None.
– No headaches?

- Flown away!
- And you don't cough at all? You coughed so much!
- Yes, my chest was torn to pieces and for months my cough troubled my neighbours' sleep . . . but I cough no more.
- And those serious haemorrhages?
- Finished.
- You have no more fainting fits or intestinal pains?
- No, now they are only sad memories.
- And you sleep now?
- Like a baby, with marvellous natural sleep.
- You feel strong at present? You had become so weak!
- Yes I was slipping rapidly into my grave. But now I feel full of vitality and courage.

My school colleagues were able to confirm this last statement, because until my retirement twelve years later, I was able to take charge of large classes, while helping my colleagues during the lunch hour. I had, little by little, done away with the midday meal, which had become useless, and this allowed me time to help others.

I continued this new diet, compiling my menus according to my work program. The greatest deficiencies being partly met, I took paps or soups of whole flour (freshly ground corn) four then three times weekly. On my rest days at home, I took the time to prepare raw food or steamed vegetables without water, whole corn or rice, buckwheat, barley and millet, varying them as much as possible.

I was never attacked by the epidemics which spread each winter in Parisian schools, such as colds, influenzas or sore throats. The tracheo-bronchitis disappeared, and the insomnia also. My blood pressure was normal. The school X-ray specialist stated that my lungs were perfect, and the aorta had become normal. The headaches and facial neuralgia from which I had suffered so much never came back, but above all, my great vitality astonished the whole school.

Then one day, for the simple reason of becoming more pure, I made a resolution to fast on Friday, a school day. On that day I felt in better form than on other days; the heavy buckets of coal I carried up to the sick neighbour, then my own coal, seemed lighter than usual.

Towards 1950, a friend advised me to read *The Auto-biography of a Yogi* by Paramahansa Yogananda. I became enthusiastic, and wrote away for the courses and later for the kriya yoga techniques. Rising early at 5 o'clock, I did my daily spiritual exercises in the morning before going to my classes and on my return in the evening. These were magnificent days. I no longer knew what tiredness was and could help my neighbours or sick friends with joy.

Before this spectacular result, several people asked me for advice. That is how I began to study different natural methods of cures by varied dieting to re-establish or preserve health, looking first, before trying them on myself, for those which seemed the most sensible to help the body regain or keep its balance.

CAUSES AND REMEDIES

"'Pre-cancerous ground' can be prepared during pregnancy if the mother is over-worked, breathes too little, eats badly or is consumed by grief, worry or anxiety. The harm is even greater if she smokes, drinks alcohol or drugs herself. The baby is then born weak and unable to fight against subsequent aggression. The vitality is further weakened if the child does not receive pure, rich maternal milk, which is very important for a good start in life. Cow's or goat's milk, pasteurized or powdered, cannot replace the mother's milk. The goodness and purity of maternal milk is evidently conditioned by the mother's own diet. If she eats correctly, the quality of her food will be a constant and considerable factor in the humoral purity (or immunity) of her child and consequently of his or her general psychical or physiological elevation." (Prof. Raymond Lautie, Doctor of Science)

The mothers of our present generation, at least in France, are feeding their babies less and less; they find it simpler to give them a bottle made from powdered milk bought at the chemist or grocer's milk, very often completely devitalized. I knew a baby in a Swiss hotel fed in this way. The child, who could not yet walk, was terribly nervous; he spent all his energy crying night and day, preventing his parents and neighbours from sleeping.

His mother was advised to give him a bottle of 'corn milk' made from corn grown without chemical fertilizer. The flour obtained from the corn, ground in a special mill, was poured together with bran into a non-metal saucepan with sufficient water to obtain a very clear pap or liquid. This liquid, to which a pinch of sea salt had been added, was sifted through a fine muslin cloth before being poured into the baby's bottle. The baby drank a big portion at once and claimed a second bottle. From that day onwards that little baby became calm and slept soundly.

From this simple experiment the mother understood that the child's food not only conditioned his health, but his character and wellbeing. The corn milk gave the child mineral salts, vitamins and other elements that had been missing and allowed him to regain his balance.

Fatigue

Whether muscular, nervous, sight or hearing, fatigue brings numerous poisons into the body. An excess of food cannot repair real fatigue. Poisons (toxins) should be eliminated by complete rest, breathing exercises, a short period of fasting or practising Louis Kuhne's method.

Air

Each day, our towns, our incorrectly heated flats, our combustion engines, our factories, our chemical culture and our nuclear experiments all combine to pollute the air and take away the necessary and essential elements, removing its energy. The smoke that covers our big towns and suburbs, even at a distance, is the cause of many epidemics and a great number of lung problems. All these intangible substances that pollute the atmosphere – sulphurous oxide gas from carbon, caustic dust from smoke, fuel oil, various sorts of soot – also cover the sun's rays. Even in clear, fine weather and during the best hours of the day, the sunlight cannot impart its biological benefits even though the sun seems to bathe the town with its light.

"Is it known that Paris is covered each month by three hundred and fifty tons of soot? This soot irritates and weakens the lungs, preparing the ground for cancer and making things worse." (Prof. Raymond Lautie)

The importance of breathing

Pure air is indispensable for the life of humans, animals and plants, for we are able to live for weeks without eating and days without drinking, but we cannot survive without air for more than a few minutes. Breathing is vital. To breathe wholesome clean air is an absolute necessity. Our food only nourishes our cells if it is oxidized. We can only transform our food into energy, with an acceptable yield free from poisonous waste, if our tissues are rich in oxygen.

Purification of our tissues is only complete if we supply enough air. It is useless to eat correctly if we breathe badly; without sufficient oxygen, no food, however correct, really benefits our cells. Deprived of this irreplaceable gas, our tissues do not remain clean, and do not live in symbiosis with their neighbours. How many excellent diets fail and are accused of being worthless because the individual ignores the art of deep breathing or lives in a confined atmosphere? Vegetarians should always keep in mind that the search for pure and vitalizing air is as important and often more so than the quest for healthy food.

Our life is only fully maintained if we perform regular daily movements and exercises (walking above all) with deep breathing. Breathing helps the complete oxygenation of each organ and also the rapid elimination of toxins. An ample breathing rhythm strengthens and protects the lungs, massages and relieves the heart, accelerates digestion, avoids digestive troubles, and strengthens and frees the liver.

To oxygenate oneself is to chase illness away; not knowing how to breathe is also one of the causes of cancer. Knowing how to breathe fully is essential, but it is also necessary that the atmosphere should not be confined or stagnant (such as in overcrowded classes, cinemas, underground railways, etc.) nor deleterious (because of soot, coal, fuel oil, petrol, etc.). By reflex we only breathe in deeply air that is clean and vivified by the sun, the ocean, balsamic perfumes (pine trees, firs, larches) or the odour of the woods. Only this natural oxygen allows complete breathing and invigorates the blood.

"Let us also look for 'air cures' as we look for real drinking water and good sound food; they reinforce our vitality and reinvigorate all our tissues." (Prof. Raymond Lautie).

Water

Water is the fundamental and indispensable liquid of life, as the normal cells in our body contain at least 75% and sometimes up to 95% water. Without it, there are no energetic exchanges, no chemical exchanges, and thus no vital activity. However, drinkable water, biologically suitable, is rarer and rarer in our towns and villages (at least in France), because polluting industries are depriving us more and more. Pollution of the air by factories, domestic smoke, engines, nuclear experiments, etc., pollution of the earth by chemical fertilizers, insecticides and pesticides, by chemical or atomic waste, contribute to the contamination of our basic drink.

Water even becomes one of the principal carriers of multiple poisons from our faulty industries and from our senseless agriculture, which have no concern for lives; as soon as water is contaminated, it is harmful to life and contributes to cancer. Real drinking water is not what we get from the taps in our towns, which is too laden with limestone, too affected by filtering agents and antiseptics like chlorine, so harmful to health. So-called 'mineral' water cannot be used for everyday needs, being too laden with varied mineral salts, and should be sold on a medical prescription. The only valuable drinking water is that collected from rocky depths

226

and containing few minerals. But again, no mineral can replace the juice of sound fruit, which still remains the best drink to entertain life.

Indeed, only vital water is active, balanced and absorbed by our cells without overloading them with salts. The plant remains the ideal apparatus for the purification and harmonization of water, on condition, however, that they are not spoiled by culture and foolish treatment (Prof. Raymond Lautie).

Healthy diet

Pure drinking water, pure air, harmonious living with balanced activity and rest, restoring sleep (before midnight) in a quiet well-aired room, absence of anxiety, worry and grief: all that is insufficient without a healthy diet. This is of utmost importance, an absolute necessity for cancer sufferers and other sick people, as well as for all those who wish to maintain their vital potential.

Cancer, said Prof. Raymond Lautie, can only establish itself in deficient organs, which are tired, and deteriorated due to faulty feeding or a way of life ill-provided with normal and healthy activities. Cancer can only set in when the blood is overladen with impurities. In fact there is only one illness, that is, illness of the blood. The quality of our blood depends on what we think, then on what we breathe, and finally on what we eat and drink.

But nearly everything we eat and drink today is charged with harmful chemical products, such as antibiotics, hormones, artificial colourings and preservatives; fruit is watered with poisonous insecticides and is indeed deadly! Sophisticated drinks modified by chemicals and artificial colouring and flavours are poisonous. Fruits and vegetables are unbalanced and deficient because of foolish agriculture and the abuse of chemical fertilizers, which eliminates magnesium, a very important factor in the struggle against cancer. (Prof. Raymond Lautie).

In his book *The Preventive Politic of Cancer*, Professor Delbet, a great French scholar who died at the age of 94, establishes that magnesium deficiency is the origin of all our sickness, and of cancer in particular. He shows that there still exist vast regions where the populations are immune to this scourge because their soil is rich in magnesium. In these countries, chiefly in South Algeria and Tunisia, the percentage of cancer is much less than elsewhere.

Magnesium deficiency paves the way for a future cancerous state, early senility and many other serious problems. Basic food is denaturalized by industrial processes: the bran and germ are taken from corn, the husk of rice is removed for bleaching and glazing purposes. Food lacking vitamins and food containing poisons and poor nourishment provoke a state of illness. It is not the only cause but the principal one.

The biological role of a healthy diet is very important. Biological nutrition consists in absorbing suitable food that supplies the myriad of cells of which our body is composed with all that is necessary to build them up, maintain and repair them, and to allow them to reproduce and carry out their specific functions. However, food should not contain anything else that is not required by the cells, for in the kingdom of the cells, all that is not useful is harmful. That means that all the substances added by our industries for different reasons to our food render it harmful.

If we do not give the human organism the exact nourishment that conforms to the need of its cells, it shows signs of deterioration little by little, and that is what doctors call 'the state of illness'. Since the vital resources in the human body are so great and since it has such an extraordinary capacity to repair itself and compensate for faulty feeding or hygiene, it takes many years to perceive the disastrous consequences of our mistakes – and that is what prevents us from understanding the true meaning of illness.

The healthy individual, who knows how to purify himself and maintain his vigour through his mental and physical wisdom, resists tumours. Nature has armed him for that. As long as his 'ground' remains normal without an excess of poison, without deficiencies, he has no fear of cancer. To prevent or cure cancer first demands the assurance of correct diet, nourishing the normal cells, oxygenating them completely and freeing them wholly of their waste. The cells need a complete food that meets all the requirements of both minerals and vitamins, a living food (Prof. Raymond Lautie), which should be raw food, fruit and vegetables eaten immediately after being picked from the garden.

Raw food

One might ask, what is the value of raw food? Dr Bircher-Benner writes: "If raw food has such efficacy, we see it above all in the increases in the cell's bio-electric tension in all the cells (tissues) of the body." These bio-electric tensions are the direct expression of the vitality of the cells (Eppinger).

Eppinger and Kunitz have shown that after a raw food cure, the cells of the tissues are capable of choosing what is best and most suitable among the substances offered, but also they have the power to refuse what is an impediment. Until now, other than raw food there are no means that allow us to increase this cellular potential and selective power. This effect seems to be attached to the freshness of the food, and our opinion on this subject is supported by modern medicine, which does not focus on the process of nutritive and vital food values, but more on the energy fresh food brings (*prana*).

The life of the food produces the life of the body; that is what characterizes the effect of raw food. In fresh food we find all vitamins in abundance and in a certain balance so that they complement each other in their effects. Very rich in vitamins A, B, C, E, F, K, P and others, fresh, raw food is particularly rich in alkaline minerals (in reserve). To all that, it is also necessary to add fermented food, the aromatic elements, the colloids, and the 'mucines', natural antibiotics, and trace elements, which have their varied effects on health. Raw food grown organically brings all these elements and many others with the minimum of toxic waste. Only raw food has these factors in a natural combination of elements that uphold and protect the cells in a manner that no artificial combination could ever compare with.

"The study of raw food is far from being complete and we are continually discovering new phenomena. More than that, fresh food appears to contain 'something', I do not know what, that is found nowhere else and which may determine all the curative actions (prana)." (Dr Bircher-Benner, *Fruit Juice and Raw Food*)

Cooking food reduces its value and makes it more difficult to digest. Cooked meals increase the number of white cells (*leucocytose*), a defensive effort that the organism automatically makes each time we eat some cooked or unnatural food on an empty stomach. The name leucocytose is derived from *leucocyte*, the technical name given to white blood cells. A cubic millimetre (mm3) of blood normally contains 6,000 white blood cells, but when we eat dead food, especially sweets and pastry of any sort, the number of white cells can double or even triple, making 18,000 per mm3. From the fact that the white cells are the defenders of the organism and appear when a danger arises, we can easily understand that the blood becomes strongly poisoned by the dead food that we eat. Leucocytes do not appear when absorbing raw food.

"Imagine the work so many white cells in the blood impose on the body. The result can be a deadly leukaemia." (Dr Christine Nolfi, *My Experiences with Living Food*) Professor Tallorico says: "We are able to state that the number of germs found in one gram of intestinal contents is about 16,500 before the digestion of a dish of green vegetables and diminishes to 2,200 after the passage of some raw vegetables."

However, the values contained in fresh raw fruit and vegetables can only fully exercise their beneficial action when the stomach is fasting or empty and the appetite not yet satisfied, and when taken alone and not mixed with cooked food.

Fasting

Every change in diet should begin with a fast, both beneficial and wholesome when one passes from a meat diet to a vegetarian diet, or a diet void of any animal product whatsoever. The learned Dr Ed Bertholet of Lausanne agrees with Dr Mayer: "Cures by fasting, miraculous cures." During the reading of numerous works, Dr Bertholet was struck by the importance given to fasting by philosophers and the wise since antiquity as a means for the purification of body and spirit. He himself had fasted on several occasions and marvelled at the results obtained from such a simple and rational practice. He gave a very complete study on the subject in his book *Return to Health by Fasting*, and specialized in this therapy.

Fasting can prove efficacious in the treatment of certain cancers, but should always be done under a doctor's guidance to avoid mishaps. Only short periods of fasting, such as one to three days, always preceded by a saline (salted water) purge may be practised without a doctor's guidance by healthy people who wish to maintain good health. One should always watch with great prudence the resumption of eating, a very delicate period which may become dangerous if good judgment is not used.

Fasting, while helping to purify the body, also develops the instinct that is reduced or totally stifled in man by so-called civilized life. It is instinct, still intact in wild animals, which allows them to choose their food according to the needs of the moment. Intuition becomes even deeper and more alive as one purifies the body. "Fasting eliminates the causes of toxicity: wrong food, medicines and vaccines." (*Clear Life,* Mr H. Ch. Gefroy.)

Dietary advice

Changing one's eating habits seems impossible to many of my compatriots. They prefer to follow their ancestral routine and absorb the food that flatters their palate and satisfies their greed, but often leads them straight to a hospital bed! Whereas, the one who wishes to be cured must know that only pure and sensible nourishment can help to eliminate illness.

231

Professor Reno (also mentioned in P. Bocquillon's book, *How One becomes Cancerous*) wrote in his book, *Why Die of Cancer?*, "It is good to know that vegetarians who always eat a certain quantity of animal products, such as milk, eggs, fish, cheese, butter . . . create in their organism a permanent toxicity that inhibits glandular secretions, and creates the possibility of irregularities in cell reproduction." For five years in one of the largest clinics in Bordeaux, Professor Reno studied the effects of different foods in the most varied pathological cases. He had the patience to study the composition of different foods and their effects on the organism with prolonged use. After 4,587 observations he determined for what reason particular foods did not have the value attributed to them, by ignorance or for ends more commercial than biological.

He possesses perfect knowledge of dietetics and healthy foods considered to be curative. Not allowing himself to be influenced by any outside factor, by ideas considered as intangible where food is concerned, his experience after more than 4,000 observations since 1924 showed him that, whatever may be said, the following foods can lead in a roundabout way to glandular deficiencies and to the much dreaded cancer.

Foods to be eliminated from the diet

Meat and fish bring to the organism terrible ammoniac poisons (purines, ptomaines, leucomaines, cholesterine (cancerous agents).

Eggs have an important quantity of lecithine, a certain material beneficial to the organism, but the advantage of which is cancelled by the massive introduction of cholesterine contained in them.

Milk is a perfect food for the calf who sucks its mother's milk, but is in general a veritable 'gelatine meat broth' (in terms of germs) when drunk several hours after milking time. Miquel informs us that immediately after milking, certain milk contains 9,000 bacteria to the cubic centimetre,

31,700 one hour later, 600,000 at the end of seven hours, and 6,900,000 after twenty-four hours. These references are for France.

'Pasteurization' or rapid heating (70° centigrade) only destroys the lactic bacilli which are necessary to stop the multiplication of putrefying germs, but does not destroy the microbial colonies remaining in the milk.

Butter and cheese contain too much cholesterine which accumulates in certain parts of our organs. This poison is found again in the biliary calucus (bladder) and in the sclerotic tissues.

Refined sugar, sweets, pastries, jams, made with chemically prepared sugar, weaken the body. Moreover, this type of sugar irritates the mucus of the stomach, has a congestive action on the liver and increases constipation by modification of the hepatobiliary mechanism. Only the natural sugar of certain vegetables and fruits assist in the upkeep of the cells. An excess of sugar prepares 'the bed of cancer'. Cancer is a tumour saturated in sugar.

White bread, which has nil food value, is a dangerous substance because it weakens and devitalizes the organism, being deprived of natural germs, mineral salts, diastases (digestive enzymes) and indispensable vitamins necessary for life.

Oats are not advised because of toxins that are too stimulating due to excessive purine. Oats are given to horses to help them run, but taken over a prolonged period oats have a heating effect and make them ill.

Polished, glazed rice loses 50–70% of its precious mineral salt, its vitamins and its diastases during the different industrial processes it undergoes; rice often brings on a tendency to constipation. It no longer has the value of whole rice in its natural form, being deprived chiefly of vitamin B which is destroyed in the process of polishing.

Alcohol, the terrible effects of which are known to all.

Coffee of which the chlorogenical acid attacks the viscus (organs situated in the chest and abdomen), raises the blood pressure or tension and hardens the arteries. It contains 1.24% of the dreaded poison, uric acid.

233

Tea brings into the organism 1.35% to 3.58% of uric acid according to its origin.

Chocolate analysis reveals up to 40% poisons (purines). Its constipating action is well known.

Coca-cola, also wrongly named as an 'economy' food, uses up physiological reserves, leading to serious organic deficiency.

Strong violent condiments, such as pepper, white salt, vinegar, spices, etc. Their exciting and irritating action on the cells can lead to gastric cancer.

Preserves (canned food) are devitalized and without any vitamins whatsoever due to hyper-cooking at 100–115° centigrade. The vitamins and the diastases are totally destroyed and vital colloidal complexes dismantled. In addition, they contain varied antiseptics and chemical substances – various acids, copper sulphate, colouring, etc. Another danger is the pollution of preserved food by the dissolution of cans covered by tin. Preserved food only presents an advantage as nourishment for travellers exploring unfrequented or deserted areas where natural food is impossible to obtain. But this role should be limited to exceptional circumstances.

All fried food is forbidden. In the case of cancer one must not absorb any heated fat whatsoever, be it animal or vegetable.

Tobacco is not a food, but is so harmful that it leads smokers more and more often to serious illness such as cancer of the throat or lungs, and also to cardiovascular trouble.

Dr Salmanoff writes: "Man is an All, a global energy, and illness is never local, it is the entire man who is ill." When pain appears, it is the third act of a drama that first began silently in the tissues. Everyone 'makes their own health' by a judicious choice of food that meets daily requirements and by a life conforming to natural laws and total hygiene.

Therefore, one should abolish harmful foods already mentioned; clothes that are air tight (such as nylon); and

234

negative thoughts (including egoism, pride, resentment, fear, jealousy, etc.). One should avoid vegetables cooked in water and in aluminium saucepans. "It has been noted that food cooked in this metal greatly increases cancerous reactions. Aluminium has been revealed as one of the greatest sources of chronic poisoning breeding cancer." (Dr Chas. L. Olda, cancer specialist, Philadelphia, USA.)

Avoid staying in polluted air or in a confined space, noise, excessive fatigue, sleeping late, and a sedentary lifestyle.

Expel poisons from the body by fasting. Sauna or sweat therapy is indispensable for eliminating organic poisons: the sweat glands should expel 2 grams of urea daily. "Sweating reduces the work of the kidneys, relieves and rests them, promotes peripheral circulation and helps the heart. By eliminating poisons it has a favourable effect on rheumatism, gout and neuralgia." (C. V. d'Autrec) C. V. d'Autrec was curious enough to have analyzed the sweat produced by ozone baths. It was always acid and often killed a rat in which it was injected, indicating its toxicity. Bromide, iodine salicylic acid, pyramidon, anti-pyrine, penol and barbiturates: veronal, gardinal, trional, etc. were found. These substances had been absorbed by patients for months or even years before, and they had never been able to eliminate them. These unnatural, foreign substances which cause serious disorder in the organism can be expelled by: Louis Kuhne's method, deep yogic relaxation and deep yogic breathing.

General purification of the organism hastens the process of a cure. Help the reconstitution of the cells by total hygiene and by an active life in pure air (walking, above all in forested land); wearing light, airy clothes; cutaneous friction (rubbing the skin), air baths, and sunbathing while lightly shaded by light foliage; perfect cleanliness of the body, baths and showers; the practice of deep breathing (yoga); leading a calm life; seeking silence; learning how to rest while completely relaxed (yoga); and sleeping before midnight (only such sleep is valuable and really restoring). In French we say, "Coucher de coq – Lever de corbeau, eloignent l'homme du tombeau", which is equivalent to the English saying, "Early to bed and early to rise makes a man healthy, wealthy and wise."

Finally, and above all, eat soundly, healthily, and wholesomely, with pure drinks (perfect drinking water or fresh fruit juice), sound food, fruit and vegetables grown organically, and complete raw or cooked cereals: wheat, corn, rice (whole), barley, millet, buckwheat, etc. Fruit and vegetables must be eaten raw as often as possible. They can be prepared in a salad with oil (varying olive oil, nut, or sunflower), a squeeze of lemon, very little sea salt, and parsley. Raw food is indispensable. Eating a little at first, chew the food well, alternating with a small quantity of whole bread (wholemeal or rye bread).

Do not eat raw and cooked food at the same time – become accustomed little by little to taking an evening meal of raw fruit or raw vegetables. If the latter must be cooked, never do so in water. As J. Reno-Bajolais indicates, "cabbage cooked in water loses 62% of its proteins, 72% calcium, 60% phosphorous and 67% iron." Raw cabbage is digested in two hours, whereas it takes four hours to digest when cooked.

In France, the mono cooker is the most perfect cooking utensil because the temperature never passes 97° centigrade and the vegetables are not in contact with water, being separated in special paper. The vegetables retain their diastases, essential oils, vitamins, ethers, particular acids and all the aromatic bodies having an action on the digestive apparatus.

Fresh fruit may be taken on waking in the morning, notably oranges for which the Arabs say "gold in the morning, silver at midday, and lead in the evening", or taken between meals. Dried fruit such as currants, figs and apricots may be taken in the evening, and almonds and other nuts in winter. All fruit is good, but chiefly grapes (black for preference) and dates, rich in magnesium, and wild fruit, richer in mineral salts than when cultivated, such as blackberries, raspberries, strawberries, bilberries.

Eat all food slowly, while thinking how it revitalizes our cells. Never eat if not really hungry or under stress or emotion, fear, grief, worry: then it is necessary to relax and return to a calm state. Become accustomed to eating meals at regular hours. Lose the habit of snacking at any time. The digestive apparatus needs rest.

A fasting day once a week is beneficial when a small laxative diet-drink is taken on waking. If one is feeling over-heavy, the day before and the day after fasting, eat only fresh fruit (a fruit diet). One should always have a clean-out before building.

Eat little. Frugality, dear to Hippocrates, is 'a source of health'. "The ancient Greeks and Romans before their fall, and the Arabs in the desert, took only one meal a day" (J. Renobajolais). The body is nourished not by what it absorbs, but by what it assimilates.

Each person should be his own diet specialist

When my health was completely restored, all my deficiencies were filled by this new form of nourishment, which seemed revolutionary to most of my friends. Thanks to living on sound food, my recovered vitality could, without inconvenience, reduce the number of my meals and the quantity eaten.

I compose my menus according to the program of the day, the work to be done and the produce I can find in Paris. It is difficult to procure sound fruit and vegetables. It is not at all troublesome for me to miss one or two meals and sometimes eat only one dish during the day. The longer or shorter 'holidays' given to my digestive system must be suitable to my organs as I don't know what it is to suffer from liverish attacks, headaches, colds or influenza. I am a very bad customer for the chemist, not having taken a single pill or any kind of drug since 1950.

There is no ideal diet, universally valid for all without distinction. Each person should learn to realize his own dietary balance, from general sound ideas together with his understanding of his own mind, body, personality, origin, education and the climate in which he lives. The food ration should be adapted to the condition of life. It varies with age, occupation, season and climate. It is necessary to keep an open mind and not shut oneself into a narrow dogma.

DIAGNOSING CANCER EARLY

Identifying cancer early enough is not as difficult as it used to be. An analysis of the blood very often shows, even before an abnormal lump is manifest, different anomalies which are significant. They prove that from the start the tumour in reality tends to unbalance and dominate the entire system of the organism, and not just one particular tissue.

Among the different methods of early diagnosis, the one which seems to be the surest until now is that of Professor Heitan of Heidelberg University. It consists of putting a drop of blood on a glass plate under a microscope (unspread) and letting it dry, then taking a colour photograph and examining the stereotype plate. The blood test is extremely simple, and on the other hand the plate with the drop of blood and the photograph are preserved for quite a time. Professor Heitan has been able to show that there is an enormous difference between a drop of normal blood and a drop of cancerous blood, with numerous stages (evolution). The techniques of early diagnosis will probably allow great progress in cancer therapy in years to come.

VACCINATION

Always more and more numerous, the most learned men of the world rise up against vaccination. After the work of Dr Pierre Oudinot, there exists a crushing dossier opposing vaccination which increases daily. Prof. Aericourt writes: "Vaccination can provoke a modification of the organic foundation by the giving way of its normal defences, that is to say, by the creation of new morbid aptitudes."

L. Claude Vincent, Honorary Professor of the Anthropologie Ecole in Paris, founder of the Bioelectronic, and appearing in 'Science of Today and Medicine of Tomorrow', says: "Anti-microbial vaccines prepare the ground for cancer, leukaemia and polio. Anti-cholera, smallpox, typhoid and BCG vaccines are very alkaline and oxidized. Their reactions correspond to the production of alpha and gamma globules of this serum. Now these are the coordinates of cancerous, leukaemic and poliomyelitic ground."

What one cannot deny after the bioelectrodigram is that the vaccine modifies the ground of the person vaccinated, pushing the individual towards an alkaline and oxidized ground, that of cancer. This fact is no longer deniable. Pasteur himself in the last days of his life said to Prof Renon: "Renon, it is Claude Bernard who is right – the germ is nothing, the ground is everything" (C.V. d'Autrec). Among European countries which have progressed most from a sanitary point of view are England, Scotland, Switzerland, Sweden, Norway and Finland, adopting the principle of freedom of choice in relation to vaccination.

YOGIC BREATHING

The learned men of India recognized thousands of years ago the astonishing results of rhythmical breathing to preserve health and protect against illness. Thanks to this type of breathing, we can learn to coax and guide the prana, a vital vibration that fills the universe. *Prana* is present in life in all forms, it is the living force, the base of all forces, including gravitation, attraction, repulsion, electricity and radioactivity. Without prana, there is no life, for prana is the source of all force and energy. This primordial principle is found everywhere in the universe. It is transported in air, but it is not air; it is found in food, but it is not food; it is the force in vitamins; it is also in water, but it is not identical to the chemical composition of water. These are only prana's vehicles.

The air is filled with free prana. Thanks to yogic breathing, we can stock a substantial quantity of prana which is then kept in reserve in our brain and nervous centres to use in case of need. This marvellous principle of life is also the original principle that engenders all mental force, chemically and physically. It is the vital cosmic force, invisible, incommensurable and indestructible. By thought we can guide prana and waken the power of healing, which is concealed in all of us.

The object of yoga is to free and develop the human values present in every human being, to stimulate the mental force and the treasures of spirituality currently lying dormant. We can easily prevent illness, and increase and preserve our vital force if we supply more fresh prana to our organism. Breath is life. When we breathe in, air enters into our body. Air contains oxygen, which is necessary for the body because of its life giving property. The life of all living beings is based on the oxygen contained in the air. If there were no oxygen in the air, all living beings would be deprived of life. Oxygen is an element which helps burning, and the process of gradual self-burning is what we call life. While inhaling, the respiratory system takes in oxygen, and while exhaling, it discharges carbon dioxide. Oxidation of the system makes the body pure, light and active.

Pranayama has a twofold effect. It helps to keep the physical apparatus pure and in good order and also to control, regulate and channel the mental-emotional being. Pranayama means controlled, rhythmic and regular breathing, which is conducive to longevity. Prana is taken to mean breath, but in reality it is the gross manifestation in the body of the subtle universal force. It is this cosmic energy which gives life to all sentient beings. The effect of prana on the human being and the correlation between the mind and the body are fully realized in yoga. Pranayama is the technique of conservation and distribution of the life force. Pranayama is indispensable for ridding the body of toxins and avoiding resulting ailments, and strengthening the corresponding organs. One who practises pranayama becomes immune to such diseases.

Thus, yogic breathing has an important part to play and a substantial, scientific and potent contribution to make in the field of physical hygiene.

SOME NATURAL THERAPIES

Below are a few methods of natural therapeutics which in certain cases may give very good results:

- The GRADE cure: see the book by Johanna Brandt (a Victor Attinger edition).
- Louis Kuhne's book on therapeutics: *The new science to cure, based on illnesses and their methodical treatment, excluding medicine and operations complying to this principle*, a work appearing in German, English, Dutch, Danish, Spanish and Portuguese.
- Cure by clay: read *Clay that Cures* by Prof. Raymond Lautie. In a wooden tub put some hot water, 30° centigrade, increasing gradually up to 39°. Add one coffee spoon full of active clay per litre, previously aerated and sun-exposed, and two grams of magnesium chloride. Bathing time: 15–20 minutes according to the patient's condition. Constantly stir the bathwater: to obtain valid effects the water should always be in motion.
- Cure by sea-water, plasma by Quintion. This was utilized in some cancer cases giving interesting results (Dr Francois Jarricgt). This doctor adds: "Thus studies are currently taking place (1966), but it is too soon to come to conclusions." Quintion's plasma certainly has a preventive role where cancer is concerned.

These different methods should be always applied with discernment and prudence according to the patient's condition.

SOME CASE STUDIES

Case No. 1

The landlord of a vegetarian hotel, who had welcomed me at Fort Romeu when I was ill, had cured himself all alone of cancer of the tongue. He had just seen his sister die a horrible death from cancer of the cheek when he perceived with great fear that a lump had formed on his tongue, worrying him more and more every day. He consulted the doctor in Perpignan, who told him, "Come back and see me in four months." The patient, little satisfied with this reply, left for Montpellier and Toulouse to consult a higher medical opinion. The answer was always the same, "Come back in three or four months." No prescription was given. The patient understood that the doctors were waiting for the volume of the tumour to increase to be able to operate. He left in utter despair for the mountains to confide in the flowers and birds. On the way, he met a friend who did him a lot of good, raising his morale and lending him a few of Professor Mono's books, one of which was entitled *Man Digs his Grave with his Teeth*. This friend said to him, "You are intelligent, read them; follow Professor Mono's advice." He did so, not taking any medicine at all, and he noted little by little the disappearance of the tumour and, to his surprise, he recovered the vitality he had had at 30 years of age – and he was over 60!

Case No. 2

A friend of mine, a lady in Geneva, Switzerland, had leukaemia confirmed by the analysis of several Swiss laboratories, an analysis requested by her doctors. My poor friend knew that she had but little time to live. She was advised to try the 'new diet': giving up meat and all animal products or by-products, and feeding herself solely on 1) whole cereals, giving predominance to corn, and 2) fruit and vegetables grown with no chemical products, and eating the food raw as much

242

as possible. She used Louis Kuhne's method to eliminate the poisons which encumbered her body, and left the city in order to rest in the pure air of the magnificent Swiss mountains, where she completed her purification. This happened in about 1952. My friend, whose recovered vitality is so great and her heart so full of charity, now spends all her time untiringly in helping others.

Case No. 3

Mr S. of Geneva is a big meat eater and heavy smoker. His wife gave the following information in a letter dated August 26, 1956: In 1951 my husband was operated on in Geneva for a duodenal ulcer, and in 1955 a malignant tumour of the tongue. He was operated on by the best known surgeons in Geneva, with the placing of eight radium points. In 1958, six more radium needles were placed. On taking the needles out after five days, the doctor saw that one of them was broken. The radium had travelled during these five days. A new operation followed, where the tongue was cut into two parts and the muscles slashed. The unfortunate man suffered horribly and was between life and death for a long time.

From a letter dated September 2nd 1959: A friend advised the patient to give up eating meat little by little, and he prudently began a vegetarian diet which his wife also adopted. However, he still smoked far too much.

A letter dated September 12th 1959 shows notable improvement. The patient feels more resistant. His appetite is coming back and his digestion is improved. Prudently, he is going to try Kuhne's baths.

Letter dated September 19th 1959: The patient suffers less from pains in the tongue and glands. He is beginning to develop an interest in life and interests himself again in his art – painting.

His wife, who had adopted her husband's new method of eating, saw with surprise that a pain in her right arm disappeared – a pain from the elbow to the shoulder which for three years no medicine had been able to cure. She no longer feels

243

anything: "What a blessing", she writes. Furthermore, since the war her thyroid gland was not working normally, for 7–14 years she had been obliged to take pills nearly every day. Now she no longer needs them: "It's miraculous!", she writes.

Letter dated October 31st 1959: The patient visits the surgeon who was greatly surprised to see the extraordinary and undeniable general improvement of his patient. He was even more astonished to see how beautiful his tongue had become! He thought that his client had been to see another doctor and he asked what medicine he had been given. He was absolutely stupefied when he learned that no pill had been taken – but he carefully took note of the diet advised, without making any comments!

Case No. 4

From *How One Becomes Cancerous* by Mr P. Bocquillon (radiologist): "A doctor begged me to take a physical X-ray of his patient. The patient, a woman, had already undergone five surgical operations for cancer of the bowels. On each occasion about 30 cm (12 inches) of bowels were amputated. In addition to faecal matter, pus and undigested food were flowing from the five wounds remaining open. The patient was in her last moments. Under the doctor's control she began treatment of a food diet based on whole or complete cereals, fresh fruits and raw vegetables, and steamed vegetables cooked without water. In a few days her condition was better and hope regained.

After two months of treatment, two of the wounds were healed. After four months, four wounds had closed and the natural functions were re-established. One wound persisted for which the doctor advised a new operation, which both the patient and her family refused. In the sixth month this last wound healed and the patient quickly regained her vitality. Now she attends to her work as a housewife, as well as gardening, sewing and occasionally travelling, without any inconvenience. The food diet is continuously observed. Our former patient has no desire to neglect herself, finding sufficient satisfaction in this way of eating and above all, a wellbeing that she appreciates above everything else."

Case No. 5

Madam L. of Tours, 65 years old in 1949, was cared for from 1949–1951 for cancer of the uterus (70% with ramification of the caecum, 70% cancerous) and the colon. The spleen and the surrenal glands and the aorta are equally attacked. A relapse of cancer occurred in spite of X-rays and radium treatment. She then commenced a natural diet advised by the radiologist, Mr P. Bocqillon and remained faithful to this until her death at the age of 84. Before her mother's death, her daughter had an immunologic analysis (a recent discovery) made of her mother's blood to know if the slightest trace of cancer remained in her mother's organism.

Case No. 6

Mr Alexander was a barrister from Madagascar who I knew from the ashram in Gretz, still young and the father of four fine boys, the eldest being twelve years old. Returning from the ashram with me, he complained of a serious loss of vitality and memory and of an intense fatigue that he could not overcome.

A lady friend gave him a little advice; firstly, to throw away all the white sugar contained in his pockets (he stuffed himself with sugar from morning to night), and secondly, to give up eating both meat and white bread. The friend promised to see him again the following Sunday in Gretz – but he did not come. He had been urgently transported to the Tenon Hospital, because of a haemorrhage so severe that it had been necessary to give him a blood transfusion and infiltrations of serum.

The doctor who greeted me when I visited the hospital showed me the X-ray pictures (he had taken me for a social assistant) and pointing with his finger on the stereotype plate, he said simply: "It's the duodenum after the second haemorrhage, the operation will be urgent." The friend gave a little further advice to the patient so that he might take care of himself after his return home. During his stay in the hospital he had the opportunity of practising a little of Luis Kuhne's therapeutics after which he was able to get up and take a little food which was meant to give him strength (food based on mashed sweet almonds and sesame seeds).

I lost sight of this patient, never having returned to Gretz, but I had the joy, a few years later, of learning that he had been able to avoid the second operation. He was well and had returned to Madagascar with his family. It is noted that by the simple diet advised, one of his sons had also cured himself of urinary incontinence, which had lasted nine years and no treatment had cured.

Case No. 7 (not cancer)

Mrs G., the sister-in-law of a friend, was 72 years old and had been weak for a long time. In periods of great depression she had frequent fainting fits. She had a distended stomach, and a porous skeleton, especially the pelvis and spine, and had suffered a myocardial infarction. She had been wearing an iron corset for five years, only walked with the help of sticks, and was very often bedridden. She accepted the care of an allopathic doctor and had numerous X-rays. She tried nourishment based on whole corn and rice, buckwheat, barley, vegetables and raw fruit grown without chemical fertilizer, and steamed vegetables. She chewed each mouthful for a long time. Little by little she gave up meat, cheese, milk and coffee. After a few weeks of this new diet, she was able to abandon her iron corset and, later on, her walking sticks.

YOGA AND CANCER

To a practitioner of yoga, an illness like cancer is not believed, primarily, to have an external cause. One of the highest aims of yoga is to control the mind. It is natural for one, even with just some experience in yoga, to think that the mind is the governing and creative factor in life. Not only does it create things that are pleasant or in accordance with our wants, but its worries are constantly hammering the mind, and it is bound sooner or later to create troubles in the body.

In order to strengthen the mind, to become aware of it and its capacities, and to gain full control over it, we will have to: 1) get the body under control and 2) control the mind from inside, through the different methods of meditation. By practising yoga asanas and pranayama, one nourishes the muscular and nervous systems, including the brain. The result is no distractions from the body, as there is nothing to worry about there, no pain, and an improved capacity to think and control the nervous energy, giving calmness and wellbeing: even if worries are there, with the nerves in order they become less important. Through meditation, peace spreads from within – the worries are being weakened and thrown out.

1. Physical approach

When a patient comes to the ashram to learn yoga and by this method cure him/herself, he will have to become accustomed to a simple way of life, simple food, getting up early in the morning and going to bed early (as is also advised here).

In India there already seems to be a method, whereby as soon as cancer was discovered, a person was sent away from the family, business and daily worries. He would live in a simple hut, and eat his meals from wooden or clay dishes, and his food should be raw and untouched by any metal. The hut should be situated in a quiet place on the banks of the Ganges river or somewhere else where there is a natural radiation of energy. Whether the energy itself was known as it is today is not certain, but like the holy and healing springs in other parts of the world, such places were also known in India.

In the ashram or with the help of a local yoga teacher, the patient (if not already having a supple body) will have to begin with simple asanas from the pawanmuktasana group.

247

Pawanmuktasana: The asanas of this series are not directly curative of cancer, but are preparatory to the later practices. The pawanmuktasana series will slowly loosen all the muscles of the body without any strain whatsoever. Part 1 of this series is called the anti–rheumatic series, which is composed of small movements where one bends feet and hands and, a little later arms and legs. Part 2 of the pawanmuktasana series is called the anti–gastric series, where one lies on the back and by bending the legs massages the intestines, removing air and toning them. After some practice the pawanmuktasana series will have prepared the body for the more advanced asanas.

Yogasanas: A great number of asanas is said to exist. In the myth Shiva taught 84,000 asanas to Parvati, his wife and pupil. In the ashram, asanas taken from a group of about 180 postures and variations will be taught. Out of the group this patient or pupil will be given his own personal little group.

As one can read here, certain food is said to eliminate toxins from the system and build up the body, and so it is in yoga. Different asanas regulate different parts of the body very effectively. Some eliminate toxins, and some tone the liver, the intestines, the lungs, the glands. For instance, sarvangasana nourishes the thyroid gland, kidneys, heart, and muscles.

Sun bath: Swami Sivananda says, "A sun bath is highly beneficial. Expose your body to the rays of the sun for a short time. Lie down on the ground on a blanket or lie on a bed. Expose your back to the rays of the sun. If the rays are very hot, cover the back with a green plantain leaf. Remain thus for fifteen minutes or till you perspire freely. This will prove useful for lumbago and rheumatism and diseases of the skin."

Pranayama, mudra and bandha: The first purpose of pranayama is to cleanse the body. In some pranayamas – bhastrika and kapalbhati – the respiratory system is cleaned so thoroughly that it is able to cure tuberculosis. Other pranayamas reduce high blood pressure and some cool the system (sometimes necessary after bhastrika, for instance).

248

One pranayama is helpful for musicians (bhramari). Pranayama cleanses and strengthens the nervous system, and controls the energy (*prana*). Cleansing the nervous system will calm the vibrations of an overworked and worried brain and relax the whole system, which is thereby able to receive the prana which pranayama 'produces'.

A further step is to control both the voluntary and involuntary nervous systems. For this there are mudras and bandhas, which are combinations of postures and breath retention, internal and external. Some are part of or preparatory to kriya yoga, which can be considered one of the direct curatives of cancer.

Before turning to the two powerful and curative yogas, kriya yoga and prana vidya, we need to know something about the mental approach.

2. Mental approach

A worry, strange idea, neurosis or sorrow which keeps on hammering the mind is sooner or later bound to cause some trouble. It is even believed that this and only this is the cause of cancer. There are glands and centres in our brain which produce secretions; some are well known to modern science (the pineal gland, for instance, provides sexual hormones to the system, etc.). Others are known to exist, but nothing is certain of their function. Experiments have shown that when certain parts of the brain are irritated, certain glands start secreting.

Now, according to yoga, concentrating on some centres (sahasrara, bindu, and ajna) can bring about good results: concentration, relaxation and illumination. Other centres are less beneficial, and if the brain is under constant strain from thoughts circulating in the mind, it may bring about nervous and physical disturbances. It is like a child and a snake. You can play with the child, but try to do the same thing with a snake!

It has been said that it is the longing for immortality which causes either liberation or cancer. But how? And why cancer? Firstly, because, it is said, we either seek through the

249

mental world towards the spiritual, or we look another way and try to establish ourselves in the material world with all our might, thinking in this way to conquer death. We do not just live a simple and natural life, but constantly worry how we can proceed into the material, forgetting even ourselves in the plans for bigger roads and buildings, and more money of course, and wishing for all the new cameras and cars. This might not be so bad in itself if only it did not keep us awake all night, and during the daytime, blinded to other human beings, to nature, to a higher reality and other life giving sources. Secondly, because according to science it seems that the only immortal cell in the body is the cancer cell nourished by a secretion from a particular centre in the brain, 'the snake' – and the only other kind of immortality is the spiritual, inside oneself, the child.

If we have worries, and most of us have – they need not of course be cancer producing – how can we get rid of them and start controlling our mentality, only thinking what we want and when we want, and thus get a better view of the whole picture?

When somebody dies in a Hindu family, immediately a lot of ceremonies take place, before, during and after the burning of the body. This is a way to divert the mind; the relatives almost forget or only think of the dead person in relation to some unforgettable feast. There are no unnatural cycles of sad thoughts in the mind, as it is constantly being interrupted by the feast and all the preparations. And now, through this picture of 'interruption', we are close to yoga and its mental approach.

The simplest, but no less effective, method of meditation is *japa yoga*, the constant repeating of a mantra, such as *Om*. It is normally given as *diksha* or initiation by the guru (spiritual guide). By repeating the mantra, it does not matter that thoughts come into the mind as long as the mind keeps on returning to and is aware of the mantra. In this way the thought process is constantly being interrupted by the same vibration (the mantra) and peace of mind is achieved.

Another method is *antar mouna*, where one watches all the thoughts coming and going through the mind, not interfering or reacting, not identifying with them, not caring whether they are good or bad. A 'seer' is being established or experienced behind the mind. It is called awareness of the real self: the 'I' which is constant behind all our experiences throughout life. That which changes are the thoughts and the mind. The result is that the stream of thoughts is being slowed down, becoming les dominant and finally stopped consciously – the mind is being cleared.

In the practice of *yoga nidra*, or psychic sleep, the body and mind become completely relaxed by the teacher's voice guiding the awareness to different parts of the body and to different mental pictures. One is, so to say, sleeping and at the same time aware of the sleep.

A further development in japa yoga is to let the mantra travel mentally through the body, in the nose and finally in the spinal cord. It is called *ajapa japa* and with the awareness of the spinal cord and its channels is preparatory to kriya yoga and prana vidya, the healing consciousness.

3. Kriya yoga and prana vidya

Common to kriya yoga and prana vidya is the controlled movement of consciousness in the body. Kriya yoga can be said to be a combination of asanas, mudras, bandhas and meditation, or rather it is neither but a yogic discipline of its own. The process of cleansing the mind is so effective and forceful here that it can only be taught under the guidance of a guru in ashram surroundings and over a certain period of time (three months minimum).

It involves the rotation of consciousness in the body. It tackles the unconscious, the subconscious and the conscious mind, and the yogi, through this method, is slowly being convinced that the mind is all powerful. That is of course a great help to one who wants to heal him/herself. And even without conviction, just from doing the kriyas, one will rebuild oneself and not be subject to disease.

251

While kriya yoga is an indirect method, bringing balance and harmony to the system as a whole, prana vidya is direct in the sense that it attacks the illness and operates right at the affected place, for instance, in the stomach. In the body the yogi has located different psychic centres, or nerve centres, and most of them are related to the glands of the body. In prana vidya we use two centres – mooladhara chakra and ajna chakra. Mooladhara chakra is situated between the anus and the urinary organ. It is the seat of energy (prana) and from here the consciousness travels up through the spinal cord, bringing energy to ajna chakra and storing it there. Ajna is situated in the brain, the pineal gland, behind the eyebrow centre. When the energy has been stored there, it is taken, through the method of prana vidya, directly to the sick part of the body.

This is what can be said about yoga and cancer in an introductory article; the rest will have to be experienced from a teacher – in the ashram, where many people have already been cured of cancer.

EXPERIMENTS BY YOSHIDA

(a Japanese cancer specialist)

In 1932 in Japan, Yoshida succeeded in provoking the appearance of cancer of the liver in laboratory rats, by adding to their usual daily rations an azote colouring of the kind readily used in the food industry. It was the first time that anyone had clearly discovered a definite chemical substance which provoked cancer when introduced into food.

So at once in Europe and the USA people tried to reproduce the experiments done in Japan, but these efforts were a complete failure. At first it was supposed that the Japanese researcher had made an error. However, as the experiment had been repeated many times with success in Japan, but with failures in Europe and America, it was wondered if there was not a difference in the experimental conditions. It was then perceived that the difference came from the usual nourishment given to laboratory rats, which in Japan were fed on polished rice with the husk and germ removed, while in Europe and America grains of whole corn were given.

It was then concluded that:

1. The action of the azote colouring contains a substance which provokes cancer, depending on the nature of the nourishment given to the subject.
2. Whole corn possesses a remarkable protective power against the action of a cancer factor or substance provoking cancer.
3. Polished rice does not possess this power.

After further research, it appeared that one of the principal protective factors contained in whole corn was represented by the Vitamin B group and more particularly by Vitamin B12 (or riboflavin). Indeed the B group vitamins are found chiefly in the germ (66%), in the bran (12–13%) and in the layer of proteins (12–13%). After processing, the white flour which remains only contains feeble traces (less than 10%).

IMPORTANT FOODS

Whole corn (with nothing removed, and cultivated without chemical fertilizer)

Corn (wheat) is the best balanced cereal for people of temperate regions. All the mineral bodies are present as in the human body and in the same proportions. Animals fed with corn cannot develop cancer or typhoid. All the elements of corn play their part as catalysts, making assimilation perfect. Bran contains silica, necessary for the pulmonary tissues. Lungs rich in silica resist consumption. The sentelium (envelope of the germ) between the embryo and the kernel contains Vitamin B1 necessary for assimilation and nervous balance. Vitamin E prevents sterility, asthma, diabetes, heart problems and certain cancers.

In whole flour, one finds: sulphur, necessary for calcium-phosphorous composition, and for the skeleton and blood; phosphorus, indispensable for the calcification of bones, tendons and teeth; sodium, which promotes digestion and assimilation; potassium, which also helps in digestion and assimilation, and the formation of blood cells; magnesium, which protects and regenerates the fibrous substance of the nerves; calcium, for bones, core of cells, blood and grey matter of the brain; iron, which supports renewal of the blood (haematosis) contributing to cell formation, leukocytes (or white cells) and haematic, also haemoglobin (pigment of the red cells); fluoride, which prevents dental decay; trace elements (substances necessary in small quantities), contributing to the transformation of food, assimilation, fixation and utilization; zinc, iodine, manganese, arsenic, copper; and vitamins: B1, B2 (regulate nutrition), B12 (anti-anaemia), E, K (anti-haemorrhage), D (anti-rickets), P.P. and carotene (which can be transformed into vitamin A).

Germinated corn contains much more calcium, phosphorous and magnesium than whole corn, and white corn contains very little. The increased activities of certain diastases allows germinated corn to be absorbed by delicate stomachs, by chewing slowly. It is a strong tonic, and a very powerful remedy. Each month, or every two or three months, one can prepare a cure, at the period of the rising moon, taking from ½–3 coffee spoonfuls a day, according to case and age, in a salad or mixed with a little honey or between meals. The most agreeable way is to mix it with salad, but never in the evening because of the richness in phosphorous. Non-vegetarians and meat-eaters should abstain from this, as should sick people whose blood pressure is too high.

The Roman Legions, who were subject to enormous weights and unbelievably long marches, carried in their belts a sachet or bag of corn and chewed a handful when they felt their strength giving out.

Corn contains all the elements required by our organism, in the germ, its vital centre, in the exterior covering or envelope, which serves as an epidermis and in all the layers of cells which form its substance.

Whole rice

Whole rice contains a little less sulphur and iron than corn, but it includes all the other minerals, except copper. It contains numerous and varied mineral substances, including phosphorous, potassium, sulphur, sodium, chlorine, magnesium, calcium, iron, fluorine, zinc, manganese, arsenic and iodine. It contains amino acetic acids and carotene (pro-vitamin A for the growth and rejuvenation of the tissues), vitamins B1 and B2, necessary for assimilation and nervous balance, vitamin P.P. (of the B complex group), anti-pellagra.

It is very rich in carbohydrate, and a remarkable energizer. Easily digestible, it can be consumed almost immediately after heavy work, a competition or other test of endurance. When combined with certain dried fruits (currants, dates, figs), it works marvels. It does not make the organism impure. Whole rice is very suitable for the aged, and its prolonged use contributes to the cure of high blood pressure (tension).

Buckwheat (saracen)

The quantity of calcium in buckwheat is superior to that of corn. It has little or no copper or manganese, but contains a large quantity of magnesium. It also contains phosphorous, fluorine (beneficial for teeth) and calcium in its very important protein amino acetic acids, which are generally only to be found in animal proteins (lystine, argirine, histidine, cystine and even tryptophane and syntonine). Saracen contains more vitamin P which strengthens the blood vessels and improves their permeability.

Medical laboratories extract rutine from saracen, forming the base of medicaments for the prevention of apoplexy. Saracen is very nutritious and exercises a welcome influence on nervous balance. It does not encumber the body or make it impure. An energizing and building food, it fortifies the blood vessels (vitamin P, citrine, which assures vascular permeability).

Professor Oshawa from Japan, a diet specialist, considers saracan favourable for the cure of cancer as well as tuberculosis.

Millet

Millet is very rich in phosphorous and is a food of choice for those who suffer from nervous depression or intellectual fatigue. In addition to this precious phosphorus, one finds a lot of magnesium and iron in millet. It is the cereal richest in vitamin A (cellular regeneration). It overcomes the deficiencies found in pregnant women and strengthens one's natural defences. Millet produces no acidity and does not fatten. Millet supplies a great number of vitamins, and is very rich in salts of calcium, magnesium, phosphorous, manganese, iron, and copper, etc. It also contains a good quantity of lecithin and free choline, valuable for increasing brain power, and contains glutamic acid which increases intelligence. Choline prevents arteriosclerosis and balances the nervous sympathetic system. It is an exceptional source of riboflavin, thiamine, and vitamins A and E.

Osborne and Mendel from Yale University, USA, have shown that millet possesses the ten important amino acetic acids indispensable for the life of our cells. Pythagoras also recommended millet to his adepts.

Barley

Barley nourishes and softens, and is also refreshing and strengthening thanks to its numerous salts: phosphorous (valuable for the nervous cells and other cells), iron, calcium, magnesium and potassium. All the mineral bodies of corn are found in varying proportions. It contains vitamins B1, B2, and P.P. which contribute to a better use of food. Its carotene (pro-vitamin A) promotes regeneration of tissues. It also helps in the calcification of the skeleton. Only use hulled barley (cleansed), not pearled barley, barley flakes or barley flour.

Malt flour is prepared from sprouted barley, dried and ground. It is a tonic for the stomach and an efficacious agent of nutrition containing a lot of vitamin B12 (anti-anaemic). For those who digest starches badly (such as pasta, potatoes, cereals, soups, etc.), it is advised to add a tablespoonful of malt flour to each portion (or plateful) a few minutes before serving. The malt flour should be added into the prepared dish and then put under a very gentle heat of 70° centigrade.

Barley soup is gentle and softening for conditions of the digestive and urinary systems. It also drains the bilious passages. For deficient intestinal functioning, take a mixture of barley as follows: 30–50 grams (½ to 2 ozs) of barley per litre (1¾ pints) of water, and add a little lemon juice.

Barley is good for nursing mothers. It is advised because of its richness in phosphorus to those lacking in muscular strength and those whose nervous system is upset. It is recommended in chronic cases of fever and irritation, pulmonary tuberculosis, haemoptysis, nephritis, cystitis, etc. A drainer of the liver, barley is most suitable for bilious temperaments.

Rye

Rye gives protection from arteriosclerotic and blood vessel illness. Rye bread promotes circulation and renders the vessels more supple. Rye is refreshing, energizing and building thanks to its richness in carbohydrate and azotic matter. It has a slight laxative and anti-haemorrhage effect. Rye bread should be made with yeast and complete flour. From the grains, a softening drink is prepared: 30 gram (1½ ozs) per litre (1¾ pints) of water. Alternate rye and wheat-corn bread in the diet.

Oats

The composition of oats is close to that of wheat-corn. It is very charged in fatty substances (carbohydrates) and in mineral salts: sodium, iron, calcium, magnesium and phosphorus. It also contains vitamins B1, B12, P.P. and carotene, as well as traces of vitamin D (anti-rickets). Oats are slightly enervating or exciting, so this food is not suitable for very nervous people. It is better eaten in the morning than in the evening. It stimulates and accelerates metabolic exchanges, which is particularly valuable in winter. It accelerates the function of the thyroid gland.

It has been used with success in muscular weakness, nervous or psychic complaints and for hyperthyroid and lymphatic conditions. It includes a hormone similar to folliculine (senna) (for impotency and sterility). Because it is diuretic, refreshing and tonic, it is advised in cases of toxicity by urea. It is recommended in diabetes for its hypoglycaemic action.

A slightly laxative diuretic drink can be made with 20 gram (about 1 oz) of oats per litre (1¾ pints) of water. Boil for half an hour. Oats can be taken as porridge or in soups.

Oats should not be given to nervous children. Racehorses are made to run by doping them with oats, but if one prolongs giving this food the animal becomes ill.

Sesame seeds

This food is of high nutritive value, and is very suitable for weak people with delicate stomachs. Rich in organic proteins indispensable for our cells it contains 18% lecithin or phosphorus vegetable fat necessary to the brain. It is this substance that produces vigorous strength. It is very rich in mineral salts, including magnesium, manganese, sulphur, iron, cobalt, copper, zinc, arsenic, phosphorus, calcium, brome, wolfram, platinum, lead, radium, and is rich in vitamins A, B1, B2, B12, C, E, F and pantothenic acid.

Sesame seeds may be eaten in their natural form or very lightly grilled and salted. When combined with other foods, sesame seeds enrich certain dishes (pumpkin, rice, etc.) and go nicely with buckwheat. A mayonnaise can be made by mixing mashed sesame seeds (or mashed almonds) with very little pure water, a small pinch of sea salt, a tiny point of mustard, a spoonful of oil and some lemon juice to taste. Sesame seeds are delicious with radishes, artichokes and tomatoes, etc. For dessert: sweetened with honey or maple syrup, and combined with a teaspoonful of pure water and a few drops of lemon. Eat very little at a time because it is an excessively rich food.

Turnsole seeds

When raw, this grain is easily assimilated. It prevents dazzling of the eyes in full sunlight. It makes the skin smooth and abolishes bleeding of the gums. It contributes to the preservation of teeth and hair and gives greater resistance to infection through its richness in silica, fluorine, calcium, phosphorus, riboflavin, and vitamins B1 and D. It contains still further minerals and trace elements, such as iron, copper, magnesium, manganese, zinc, and cobalt, etc. Peeled and very lightly grilled, it can be eaten like peanuts.

Bibliography

Bertholet, Dr Ed, *Coming back to Healthy Life by Fasting*

Bircher-Berner, Dr, *Fruit Juice and Raw Food*

Bocquillon, Pierre, *How One becomes Cancerous*

Kuhne, Louis, *The New Science of Curing based on the Unity of all Illnesses* (in German, English, French, Dutch, Danish, Spanish and Portuguese)

Lautie, Prof. Raymond, Doctor of Science, *The Air we Breathe; The Water we Drink; The Atomic Danger & Among Beneficial Plants*

Lorence, V. & Laboulais J., *The Overtonian Poisons*

Nolfi, Dr Christine, *My Experiences with LivingFood*

Oudinot, Dr Pierre, *The Conquest of Health*

Reno-Bajolais, J., *Modern Techniques of Rational Human Feeding*

Saraswati, Swami Satyananda, *Dynamics of Yoga*, Yoga Publications Trust, Munger, Bihar, India

References

Chapter 3

[1] Garssen, B., Psychological factors and cancer development: Evidence after 30 years of research. *Clinical Psychology Review,* 2004, 24(3):315–338.

[2] Antoni, M.H., Lutgendorf, S.K., Cole, S.W. et al. The influence of bio-behavioural factors on tumour biology: Pathways and mechanisms. *Nature Reviews Cancer,* 2006; 6(3):240–248.

Chapter 6

[3] Pert, Candace, *Molecules of Emotion,* Simon and Schuster, 2003.

[4] *Science Update,* Studies Identify Subtle Genetic Changes' Risk for Mental Disorders; May Lead to Targets for New, Better, Therapies. National Institute of Mental Health (USA), May 05, 2008.

[5] Day, Phillip, *Cancer – Why We're Still Dying to Know the Truth,* Credence Publications, UK, 2005.

Chapter 34

[6] Vakhrusheva, O. et al, 'Sirt7 increases stress resistance of cardiomyocytes and prevents apoptosis and inflammatory cardiomyopathy in mice'. *Circ. Res,*. March 2008, 102 (6): 703–10.

Lane, David, Genome informatics 2007, *Genome Informatics Series*, Vol. 19, pp194.

[7] Wallace, D.C., *Cold Spring Harb Symp Quant Biol.* 2005, 70:363–74.

[8] Brandon, M., Baldi P., Wallace D.C., *Oncogene*, 2006 Aug 7;25(34):4647–62.

[9] Simone, Charles, *Cancer and Nutrition*, Avery Publishing, New York.

[10] Quillin, Patrick, *Beating Cancer with Nutrition: Clinically Proven and Easy-To-Follow Strategies to Dramatically Improve Quality and Quantity of Life*, http:/www.healthy.net. From the M. D. Anderson pamphlet 'Road Map to Cancer Prevention.' http://www.mdanderson.org/

[11] Robinson, A.B. et al. Suppression of squamous cell carcinoma in hairless mice by dietary nutrient variation. *Mech. Ageing Dev.*, 76 (1994) 201–214.

[12] Sareen, S., Kumari, V., Yoga for Rehabilitation in Chronic Pancreatitis. *Gut*, 55(7):1051.

Rajesh, B., Jayachandran, D., Mohandas, G., Radhakrishnan, K., A pilot study of a yoga meditation protocol for patients with medically refractory epilepsy. *Journal of Alternative and Complementary Medicine*, 12(4):367–71.

Ott, M.J., Norris, R.L., Bauer-Wu, S.M., Mindfulness Meditation for Oncology Patients: A Discussion and Critical Review. *Integrative Cancer Therapies*, 5(2), 98–108.

Malhotra, V., Singh, S., Tandon, O.P., Sharma, S.B., The beneficial effect of yoga in diabetes. *Nepal Medical College Journal*, December 2005, 7(2):145–7.

Kirkwood, G., Rampes, H., Tuffrey, V., Richardson, J., Pilkington, K., Ramaratnam, S., Yoga for anxiety: a systematic review of the research evidence. *British Journal of Sports Medicine*, December 2005, 39(12), 884–891.

Pilkington, K., Kirkwood, G., Rampes, H., Richardson, J., Yoga for depression: The research evidence. J. Research

261

Council for Complementary Medicine, London, UK, *Journal of Affective Disorders*. Published online (ahead of print) Sep. 23 2005.

Sabina, A.B., Williams, A.L., Wall, H.K., Bansal, S., Chupp, G., Katz, D.L., Yoga intervention for adults with mild-to-moderate asthma: a pilot study. *Annals of Allergy, Asthma, and Immunology*, 94(5):543–8.

Bibliography

Ashley-Farrand, Thomas, *Healing Mantras: using sound affirmations for personal power, creativity and healing*, The Ballantine Publishing group, USA, 1999.

Day, Phillip, *Cancer: Why We're Still Dying to Know the Truth*, Credence Publications, UK, 2005.

Guyton, Arthur, *Textbook of Medical Physiology* 8th edn, W.B. Saunders Company and Prism Books (Pvt) Ltd, Bangalore, 1991.

Isselbacher, Kurt et al, ed. *Harrison's Principles of Internal Medicine*, 13th edn, McGraw Hill, Inc., USA, 1994.

Kumar, Vinay et al, *Basic Pathology*, W.B. Saunders Company and Prism books (Pvt) Ltd, Bangalore, 1992.

McMinn, R.M.H. ed. *Last's Anatomy, Regional and Applied*, Churchill Livingstone, New York, 1994.

Morgan, Clifford et al, *Introduction to Psychology*, Tata McGraw Hill Publishing Co. Ltd, New Delhi, 1999.

Park, J.E. & Park, K., *Park's Textbook of Preventive and Social Medicine*, M/s. Banarsidas Bhanot, Jabalpur, 1991.

Pert, Candace, *Molecules of Emotion*; *Why you feel how you feel*, Simon and Schuster, New York, 2003.

Sannyasi Gyanshruti & Sannyasi Srividyananda, *Yajna, A Comprehensive Survey*, Yoga Publications Trust, Munger, Bihar, 2006.

Swami Muktibodhananda Saraswati, *Hatha Yoga Pradipika*, Yoga Publications Trust, Munger, Bihar, 2000.

Swami Niranjanananda Saraswati, *Dharana Darshan*, Yoga Publications Trust, Munger, Bihar, India, 2006.

Swami Niranjanananda Saraswati, *Prana Pranayama Prana Vidya*, 3rd edn, Yoga Publications Trust, Munger, Bihar, 2002.

Swami Satyananda Saraswati, *Amaroli*, 2nd edn, Bihar School of Yoga, Munger, Bihar, 1991.

Swami Satyananda Saraswati, *Asana Pranayama Mudra Bandha*, 4th edn, Yoga Publications Trust, Munger, Bihar, 2008.

Swami Satyananda Saraswati, *Kundalini Tantra*, Yoga Publications Trust, Munger, Bihar, 2002.

Swami Satyananda Saraswati, *Meditations from the Tantras*, 2nd edn, Yoga Publications Trust, Munger, Bihar, 2000.

Swami Satyananda Saraswati, *A Systematic Course in the Ancient Tantric Techniques of Yoga and Kriya*, Yoga Publications Trust, Munger, Bihar, 2003.

Swami Satyananda Saraswati, *Yoga Nidra*, 6th edn, Yoga Publications Trust, Munger, Bihar, 2001.

Dhyana Yantras: Tools for Meditation, 2nd edn, Yoga Publications Trust, Munger, Bihar, 2007.

Williams, Peter, & Dyson, Mary, ed. *Gray's Anatomy*, Churchill Livingstone, Great Britan, The Bath Press, 1992.

Resources from the Web
1. National Institutes of health and National Cancer Institute: http://www.nci.nih.gov
2. Nutrition and Cancer: http://www.mdanderson.org
3. NCI Cancer bulletin, November 28 2006: http://www.cancer.gov
4. http://www.training.seer.cancer.gov
5. http://www.cancernaturalcure.com
6. American Cancer Society: http://www.cancer.org

7. The Cancer Nutrition handbook: http://www.cancernutrition.com.
8. Psychoneuroimmunology: http://en.wikipedia.org.
9. Cellular respiration: http://en.wikipedia.org.
10. Dr. Len's Cancer blog: http://www.cancer.org
11. Research abstracts on mitochondria and cancer: http://www.ncbi.nlm.nih.gov.
12. Alternative Medicine foundation: http://www.amfoundation.org.
13. Stress and Cancer: http://www.psychcentral.com.
14. The Mind-body connection and Cancer: http://www.oralcancerfoundation.org/emotional/mind-body.htm
15. pH and Cancer: http://www.alkalizeforhealth.net/index.htm

— Notes —

— Notes —